THE DESIGN AND CONSTRUCTION OF THE

NAUTILUS

THE DESIGN AND CONSTRUCTION OF THE
NAUTILUS

THE SUBMARINE TECHNOLOGY
OF JULES VERNE REVEALED

DEMETRI CAPETANOPOULOS

3rd Edition

Book Design & Production
Columbus Publishing Lab
www.ColumbusPublishingLab.com

LCCN 2018956680

Hardback ISBN: 978-1-63337-220-7
E-book ISBN: 978-1-63337-221-4

Printed in the United States of America
13 5 7 9 10 8 6 4 2

"The Devil is in the details, but so is salvation."

— Admiral Hyman G. Rickover
"Father of the Nuclear Navy"

FOREWORD

Imagine yourself living in the 1850s, some 165 years ago, at the dawn of a century of technological innovation and progress. This was the time of Jules Verne. Through imagination and a keen eye for the changes—in technology, society, and politics—invading his world, he created a story, a rich legacy that continues to capture readers to this day. His publication of *Twenty Thousand Leagues Under the Sea* in 1870 was a worldwide sensation. A fictional tale, the submarine *Nautilus*, under the command of Captain Nemo, embarked on an epic adventure. The story is narrated by Professor Pierre Aronnax, who throughout the course of the novel describes many technical details of the mysterious and marvelous *Nautilus*.

Today we too easily consign Verne's creation to the realm of science fiction or even fantasy. But what if his submarine, the *Nautilus*, was viewed as less science fiction, and more the enlightened vision of what might have been possible? Who among us has not imagined what it might be like to embark on such adventure? Imagined what an actual submarine of Jules Verne's day might have been like? And wondered how, by combining and integrating the technologies of the mid-19th Century, a real submarine might have been built? In this book, *The Design and Construction of the Nautilus*, you will "design," with the author, Verne's *Nautilus*. With the help of today's knowledge of engineering disciplines, naval architecture, and submarine technology you will see the result—a futuristic vessel (for that epoch) embedding the most advanced technologies of the mid-19th Century. You will explore the state-of-the-art science and engineering that would have been required to build a real *Nautilus*. For that era, she would have been the most sophisticated machine in existence; not unlike today's modern nuclear submarines, which are the most complex machines on our planet; true technological marvels.

It is worth saying that this book is about the history of submarine technologies, and not about Jules Verne and his stirring tales of adventure. The focus is on exploring how the technologies of Verne's time could have been used to actually build the submarine of Verne's creation. The author, a submariner and engineer in his own right, blends today's knowledge of submarine design and engineering, and creates for us an intriguing look into the possibility that the *Nautilus* could actually have been designed and built in the mid-19th Century. Captain Capetanopoulos brings to us a vision of a submarine able to sail the Seven Seas at will, independent of the land and its peoples, and in the process convinces the reader that Jules Verne, well beyond being just a novelist, was an accomplished futurist, well versed in the myriad technologies emerging in the 1800s across Europe and the Americas. Guided by the narrative of Professor Aronnax, witness to all of the *Nautilus's* travels, Captain Capetanopoulos shows us, in text, blueprints, and detailed drawings, how the *Nautilus* might actually have been constructed.

In Verne's time, the idea of traveling the seas by submarine was entirely new, with few in the world able to think how this might be possible, much less able to consider what it might take to actually build and operate a vessel able to cruise beneath the waves. Yet, in his *Twenty Thousand Leagues Under the Sea*, Jules Verne opens to our senses a fantastic vision of the future. He astounded readers with his descriptions of a vessel able to sail on its own across the world's oceans, deep beneath the surface, at a time when use of electricity, steam power, electromagnetism, useful battery power, and deep-sea diving were first being explored.

In my own career in the Submarine Service, I served on five submarines, went to sea on both U.S. and German diesel submarines, contributed to the design of the *Seawolf* class, and in the process experienced and made use of the complex technologies necessary to operate today's nuclear submarines safely in the depth of the world's oceans. My adventures were real, encompassing Atlantic waters and the vast expanses of the Pacific and beyond. In the course of things, we tested the limits of our technology, its capabilities, and the crews with whom I served. It is amazing to me to see a design of the *Nautilus* brought to life in this book — a design based on 1800s technologies, but adhering to principles of engineering and technology adaptation that remain relevant to the design, construction, and operation of today's state-of-the-art nuclear fast attack and fleet ballistic missile submarines. For history buffs and engineers alike, reading *The Design and Construction of the Nautilus* is an immersion in a bold tale of adventure from a technology perspective. As surmised above, *Twenty Thousand Leagues Under the Sea* is a fictional tale, but what if Captain Nemo's *Nautilus* could have been real?

— Richard J. Severinghaus

Commander, USN (ret.), CMSP
Former Commanding Officer, USS *Annapolis* (SSN 760)
and Staff Engineer, Naval Reactors HQ, NAVSEA 08

GUIDE TO THE EXPLORATION OF THE NAUTILUS

Nautilus pompilius

Nautilus—a pelagic marine mollusk, of the cephalopod family Nautilidae, found only in the Indo-Pacific. By regulating water within an internal chamber it is able to maintain neutral buoyancy and adjust depth at will. Having survived relatively unchanged for millions of years, they are often considered "living fossils." The word nautilus is derived from the Greek word for "sailor."

INTRODUCTION

Is there anyone, of any age, who has read *Twenty Thousand Leagues Under the Sea* and not sketched their vision of the *Nautilus* in their imagination or down on paper? For 150 years, the submarine created by Jules Verne has captivated readers and inspired countless interpretations. But with time, the *Nautilus* has become viewed as increasingly fanciful, to the point of being dismissed outright as impossible. That is unfortunate because Verne, whose work arguably created the genre of science fiction, was meticulous about incorporating cutting-edge technology of his time and making reasonable extrapolations. Though his literary legacy endures, our distance from that era of industrial and technological frenzy has dulled our ability to fully appreciate the marvelous vision that is the *Nautilus*. These plans and the notes that follow attempt to place Verne's imaginative creation in context with his times to enable the most complete and accurate reconstruction of the *Nautilus* possible. To this, a healthy dose of modern submarine design insight has been added to ensure the *Nautilus* remains relevant and accessible as it sails into its next 150 years. For the *Nautilus* is more than just a 19th century mechanical marvel. To those who have sailed storied pages with her, she has always represented the ultimate technological triumph over nature, symbolizing mankind's mastery of our domain, the human desire to explore the unknown, and most of all, freedom.

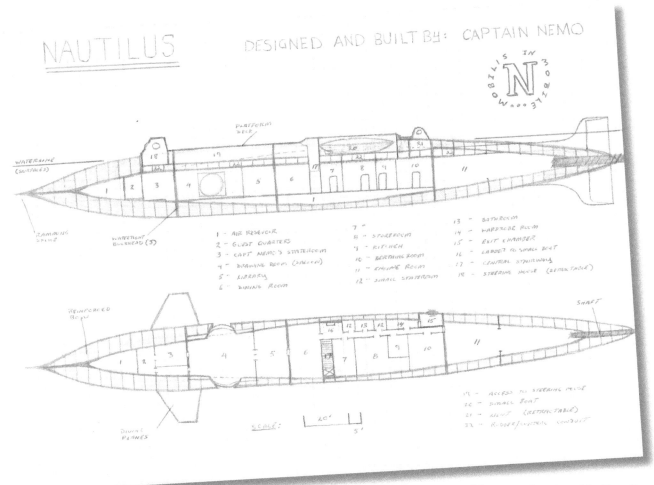

My own exploration of the Nautilus
began around age ten with this sketch.

EARLY SUBMARINE DEVELOPMENT

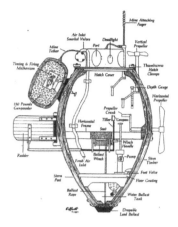

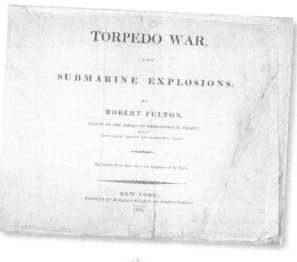

...it was an effort of genius; but that a combination of too many things were requisite, to expect much success from the enterprise against an enemy...

Bushnell's *Turtle* 1775

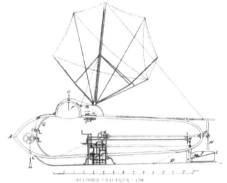

Fulton's *Nautilus* 1800

Payerne's *Belledonne* 1846

Bauer's *Sea Devil* 1855

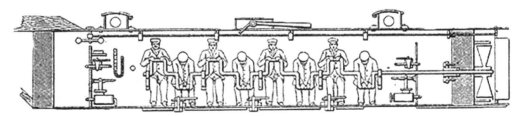

McClintock's *H.L. Hunley* 1863

Accounts of mankind venturing beneath the sea enclosed in a mechanical vessel date back to Aristotle in the 4th century BC. But the attempt to construct a submarine boat that could serve as an effective weapon has a relatively short history punctuated with few successful examples. By the time Jules Verne began to imagine a voyage of 20,000 leagues under the sea, submarine warfare had only the partial success of the *Turtle* and the *Hunley* to offset the inadequate performance of Fulton's *Nautilus*, Bauer's *Brandtaucher* and *Sea Devil*, and a slew of Union and Confederate semi-submersible ships and submarine boats. No one else at that time could conceive of a submarine as anything other than tiny, exhausting and hazardous to operate, and more a threat to its crew than to an enemy ship.

In April 1863, the French submarine *Plongeur* was launched, providing a hint of what was to come. She was the first submarine to be propelled by mechanical rather than human power; possessing a reciprocating engine driven by compressed air. The air was stored in twenty-three tanks, which resulted in a submarine of enormous proportions. At 140 feet (42.7 m) she was more than three times larger than *H.L. Hunley*. *Plongeur* was equipped with a ram for attacking ships and pioneered the use of compressed air to dispel water from the ballast tanks. She also had a small lifeboat integrated into the upper part of her hull. Although her stored energy provided very limited endurance and her depth control and stability were unsatisfactory, she heralded a period of rapid submarine experimentation and development. A model of *Plongeur* was displayed at the 1867 Exposition Universelle in Paris where it was studied by Jules Verne, inspiring his conception of a submarine and serving as a model for the *Nautilus*.

With these tentative but promising steps as our point of departure, let us begin our exploration…

Plans for the submarine Plongeur

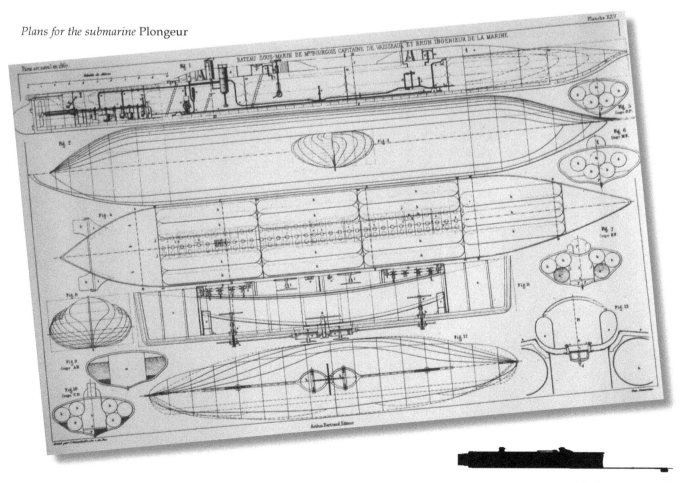

H.L. Hunley *to scale*

The Sydney Morning Herald

WEDNESDAY, AUGUST 2, 1866.

SCOTIA DAMAGED DURING ATLANTIC CROSSING

Holed by unseen hazard

Arrives Liverpool 3 days late

All aboard safe

On April 16 the Cunard liner Scotia arrived in Liverpool after a most eventful Atlantic crossing. Just three days earlier, the record-setting ship experienced a collision with an unseen hazard in the open ocean that was sufficient to rupture her immensely strong hull and resulted in significant flooding. Only the skill and bravery of Captain Anderson and his crew prevented a complete loss and enabled the vessel to reach port safe and sound. This shocking incident represents a first for the Cunard line in twenty-six years of operation and over two thousand Atlantic crossings. The collision occurred during daylight, in good weather, while the Scotia was running under steam power and making approximately thirteen knots. Cunard Co. has indicated that the ship will be placed in dry dock and that a complete investigation is to be conducted. Despite the unusual circumstances, the conduct of Captain Anderson has thus far not been subject to question. It is uncertain when Scotia will resume her scheduled crossings and the Cunard Co. has directed all passenger inquiries to its Liverpool office.

A curious report was received from the captain of the Cristobal Colon of the West India & Pacific Steamship Co. which recently arrived in Sydney harbor. He reports that on July 23, while steaming some 700 leagues to the East he came upon what appeared to be a semi-submerged rock perhaps two hundred feet in length. Approaching to better fix the position of this hazard for future navigation, the rock shifted its position as if it were afloat and then emitted two large geysers of water before disappearing from view. This report bears an uncanny familiarity to one made by Captain Baker of the steamer Governor Higginson from the Calcutta & Burnach Steam Navigation Co. a few days earlier, of a moving reef spouting great columns of water just five miles off of our eastern coasts. Both captains reacted indignantly when it was suggested that these were confused whale sightings and admittedly, a second such report from a notably distinguished observer cannot be easily dismissed.

Shipping News

The SS Moravian of the Montreal Ocean Company reported sustaining a collision at sea on March 3. The vessel is returning under its own power to Montreal but its expected to be delayed by at least two days due to the damage. Initial reports indicated the ship was making thirteen knots, in waters not known to contain any hazard, when it was violently struck from astern.

The SS Nova Scotian, under the command ... gan Wylie, is now expected to depart not

August 8, 1866

The Daily Telegraph

2

ROGUE CETACEAN MEASURES 380FT

Two ships simultaneously sight the mysterious monster

The mysterious sea creature that has been responsible for numerous ship collisions over the past year was sighted by two ships making a definitive measurement possible. The S.S. Shannon of the Royal Mail Steam Packet Co. and the S.S. Helvetia of the National Steam Navigation Co. encountered the creature simultaneously during their transatlantic crossings in vicinity of latitude 42° 15′ north and longitude 60° 35′ west of the meridian of Greenwich. The two ships, travelling in opposite directions, were able to maneuver close enough to the giant cetacean to permit a careful inspection of its size. The captains of both vessels definitively agreed that the creature exceeded the length of both the Shannon, length 338 feet, 3,609 tons displacement and the Helvetia, 371 feet displacing 3,318 tons. There can be no doubt now that this is a marine species unknown to science and one which poses an undeniable hazard to shipping the world over. The widespread sightings of this creature suggest that they are numerous and broadly distributed in the oceans. That deadly encounters are not been recorded previously can be due to improved communications and increasing presence of ship [ ] traveling the water[ ]

LONDON, THURSDAY.

Engineers were astonished to discover the nature of the damage sustained to the Cunard liner Scotia during her most recent Atlantic crossing. The collision, which occurred on April 13, produced a two meter hole in the iron hull that was inexplicably formed in the shape of a perfect isosceles triangle. Such a hole could only be the result of a most powerful punch and is further confounded by the fact that whatever produced it had to be withdrawn from the hull as no trace of the cause was left behind to be discovered. The strange incident has resurrected speculation that a heretofore unseen cetacean of monstrous proportions was roaming the oceans after the rash of sightings reported last year. But given the speed and strength required to hole Scotia's hull, a biological protagonist seems unlikely. Are we then compelled to believe that a mechanical contrivance, operated by an unidentified adversary is at loose in the oceans? The Admiralty has ad[ ]

Aux premières heures du mardi matin, le vapeur Normandie aperçut une puissante lumière située près de la surface de l'océan à environ deux cents milles au nord des îles Canaries. Elle se referma sur la lumière mais à l'aube, elle s'éteignit rapidement. La source de la lumière a accéléré rapidement dépassant la meilleure vitesse de la frégate de treize nœuds, et a été perdue de vue. En raison du caractère inhabituel de cette rencontre, la Marine Nationale demandé un rapport officiel.

THE NEW YORK

NEW YORK, SATURDAY.

WAR DEPARTMENT DECLARES USS ABRAHAM LINCOLN LOST AT SEA

After four months with no communication from the frigate, the War Department has of[ ] [ ] the USS Abraham Lincoln [ ]

no survivors from among the two hundred and eighty nine officers and crew, which included at least two foreign civilian passen[ ]

NEW YORK H

EUROPEAN EDITION—PARIS, SATURDAY, MARCH 25, 1905.—EIGHT PAGES

[PRO]FESSOR WHO TOLD TALE OF AMAZING [U]NDERWATER VOYAGE DEAD AT 78

Professor Pierre Aronnax of the Muséum national d'Histoire naturelle passed away quietly at his home in Amiens yesterday. A leading expert in the field of marine biology, he authored numerous books on the subject including The Mysteries of the Great Ocean Depths which went through seven revisions. But he is perhaps best known for his account of how he and two companions survived the loss of the USS Abraham Lincoln and subsequently spent ten months voyaging beneath the sea in an incredible submarine boat named Nautilus. The subsequent lack of any corroborating evidence eventually led many to discredit the account which his more vociferous critics claimed was nothing more than a publicity stunt to rekindle his celebrity. Frustrated by a skeptical public that increasingly treated his tale as entertaining fiction, he withdrew from public appearances and focused increasingly on his work. By all accounts his later years were some of the most productive to science and his insights and predictions of deep ocean discoveries continued to astonish colleagues even following his formal retirement in 1890. Professor Aronn[ax is not] known to have left any surviving family.

A16 Thursday, Jul 24, 2016

TANGIER PREPARES TO GREET KAISER.

Decorations on Extensive Scale [ ] a Proceeding Apace in Vari[ ] [ ]us Quarters of City.

MEETING OF BRITISH COLONY.

Thursday, Jul 24, 2016 THE WASHINGTON POST

History Succumbing to South China Sea Island Construction

BEIJING — Despite the international tribunal ruling earlier this month rejecting recent claims of sovereignty there doesn't appear to be any intent to slow infrastructure development on islands throughout the South China Sea and that has some worried about not just environmental impact but also potential historical loss. Despite the fact that few islands of the Paracel Archipelago have any history of habitation, satellite imagery of at least one island show remains of unexplained structures and evidence of human use that may date back one hundred years or more. These discoveries on Lincoln Island are at risk as new roads and other construction is rapidly changing the landscape. Archeologists who have examined the photos suggest that the site may have served as a camp for itinerant fisherman seeking a protected spot to repair their vessels, though they acknowledge that what remains of the structures appear to have been built on a scale inconsistent with such transient

ISLAND continued on B3

The Cork E[xaminer]

THURSDAY MORNING, JULY 6, 186[6]

RESCUED AFTER TEN MONTHS IN THE BELLY OF A BEAST!
SOLE SURVIVORS OF USS ABRAHAM LINCOLN TELL AN AMAZING TALE

More than ten months after the American frigate was declared lost somewhere in the Pacific with all hands, three of her passengers have been recovered by Lofoten Islanders from a Maelstrom in the far Northern Atlantic! Professor Aronnax of the Paris Museum of Natural History, his man-servant, and a Canadian embarked aboard as a harpooner, are apparently the only survivors of a maritime disaster precipitated by an insane genius bent on exacting vengeance from the civilized world. According to their account, the frigate was rammed by an incredible iron submarine of im-

mense size and power. Cast into the sea by the collision, they were forced to take refuge aboard the submarine, becoming involuntary guests of Captain Nemo, the mysterious commander of this mechanical marvel held them captive for ten months as he roamed the seas waging his reign of terror against hapless shipping the world over. This then is the long awaited explanation for the rash of mysterious sightings and unprovoked collisions that have been the cause of much consternation and speculation these past few years. Yet it scarcely seems possible that an undersea craft of such size and sophistication could have been

crafted in secret by a single individual. And not just a utilitarian machine of war, but as told by Professor Aronnax, a floating palace and museum containing immeasurable treasures. Surely such descriptions are hyperbole, reflective of the survivor's pronounced relief at their escape and rescue. Additional details are difficult to obtain as the professor is in route to Paris. There he is expected to give a public talk detailing his adventures and a published account is said to be forthcoming. No doubt it will be eagerly received but whether it is accepted as incredible fact or fantastical fiction is yet to be determined.

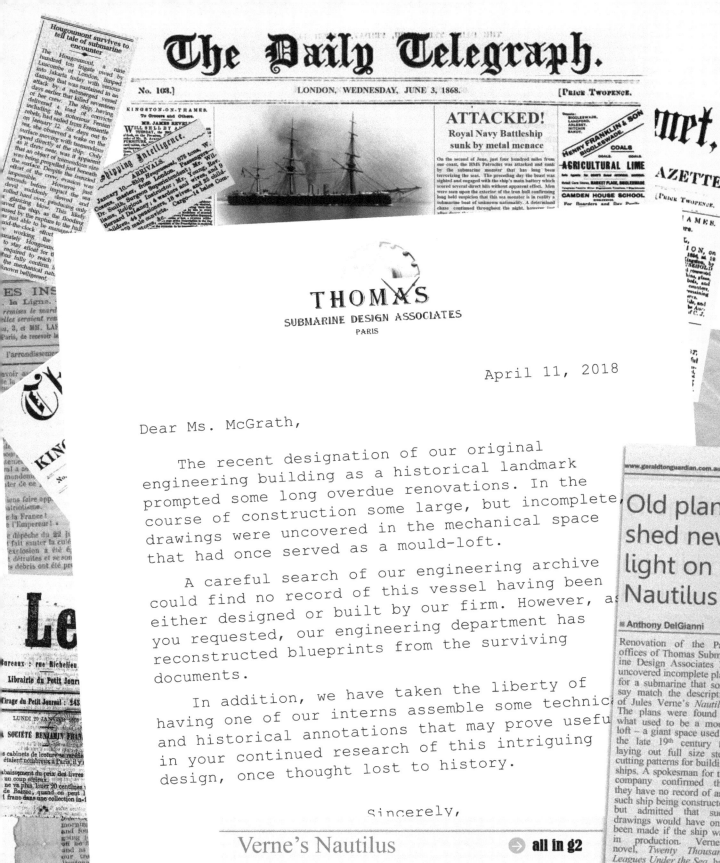

The Daily Telegraph.

No. 103.]   LONDON, WEDNESDAY, JUNE 3, 1868.   [PRICE TWOPENCE.

ATTACKED!
Royal Navy Battleship sunk by metal menace

On the second of June, just four hundred miles from our coast, the HMS Patroclus was attacked and sunk by the submarine monster that has long been terrorizing the seas. The preceding day the beast was sighted and engaged with the ship's main battery which scored several direct hits without apparent effect. Men were seen upon the exterior of the iron hull confirming long held suspicion that this sea monster is in reality a submarine boat of unknown nationality. A determined chase continued throughout the night, however ...

THOMAS
SUBMARINE DESIGN ASSOCIATES
PARIS

April 11, 2018

Dear Ms. McGrath,

The recent designation of our original engineering building as a historical landmark prompted some long overdue renovations. In the course of construction some large, but incomplete drawings were uncovered in the mechanical space that had once served as a mould-loft.

A careful search of our engineering archive could find no record of this vessel having been either designed or built by our firm. However, as you requested, our engineering department has reconstructed blueprints from the surviving documents.

In addition, we have taken the liberty of having one of our interns assemble some technical and historical annotations that may prove useful in your continued research of this intriguing design, once thought lost to history.

Sincerely,

Old plans shed new light on Nautilus

■ Anthony DelGianni

Renovation of the Paris offices of Thomas Submarine Design Associates has uncovered incomplete plans for a submarine that some say match the description of Jules Verne's *Nautilus*. The plans were found in what used to be a mould loft – a giant space used in the late 19th century for laying out full size steel cutting patterns for building ships. A spokesman for the company confirmed that they have no record of any such ship being constructed but admitted that such drawings would have only been made if the ship was in production. Verne's novel, *Twenty Thousand Leagues Under the Sea*, has always been considered fiction, however this discovery has some suggesting that perhaps it may be a true account, something Prof. Arannox maintained until his death in 1905. This week, his grand-niece, Ms. Diane McGrath, has announced she is funding a reconstruction of the plans to determine whether such a machine could have actually been constructed. The ...

Verne's Nautilus   ➔ all in g2
Discovery prompts new questions about old work thought to be fiction

Top View

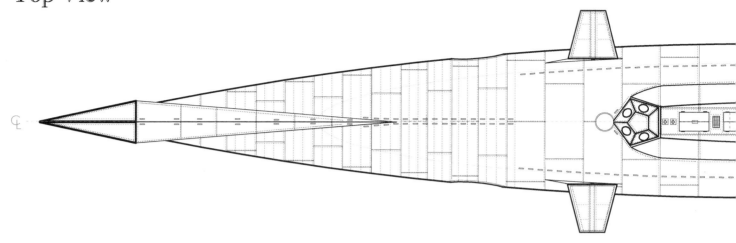

Port Side View

Waterline

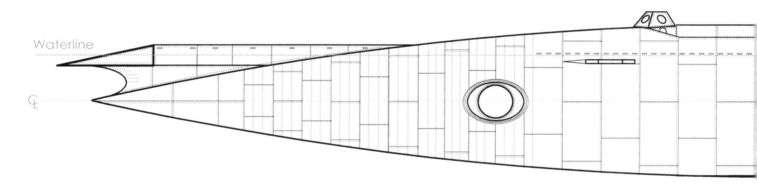

Bow View

Waterline

Stern View

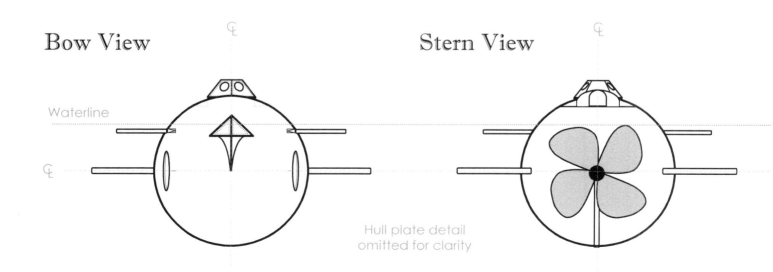

Hull plate detail
omitted for clarity

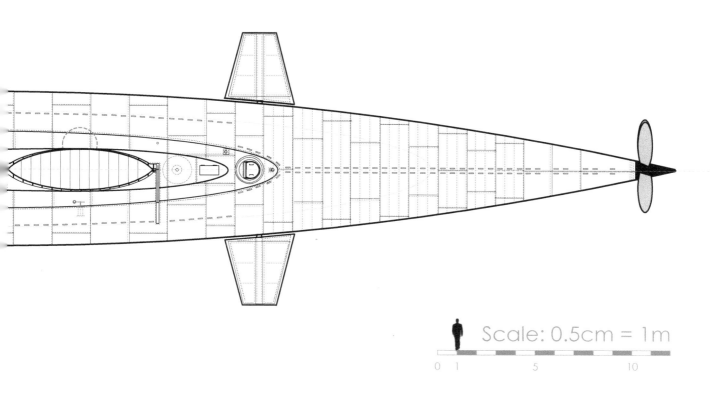

Scale: 0.5cm = 1m

0   1   5   10

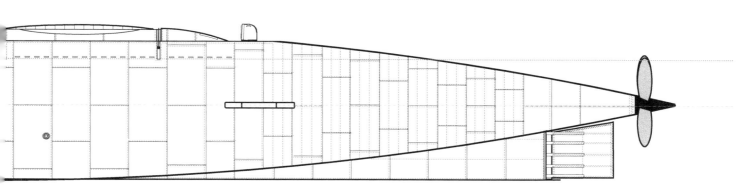

The

Nautilus

MOBILIS
N
IN MOBILE

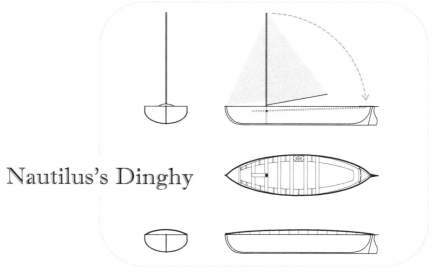

Nautilus's Dinghy

Inboard Profile

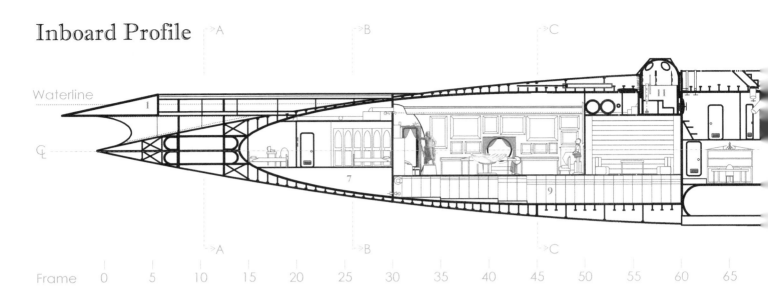

Waterline

A   B   C

1   11

A   B   C

Frame 0 5 10 15 20 25 30 35 40 45 50 55 60 65

7   9

Plan View: Upper Deck

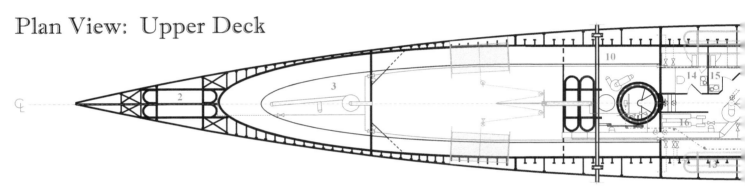

2   3   10   14 15   16   13

Plan View: Lower Deck

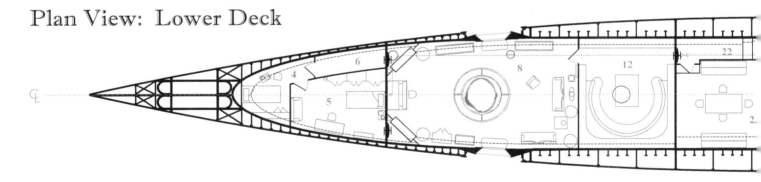

4   6   22
5   8   12   2

Cross Sections

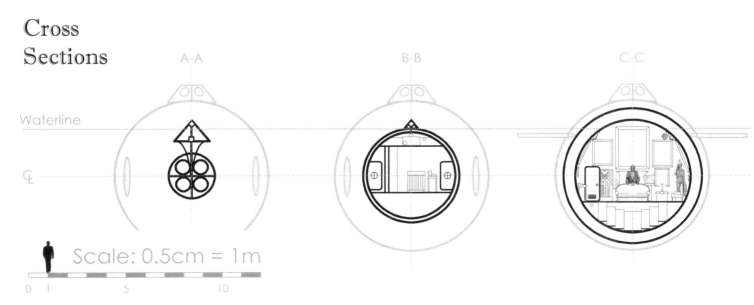

A-A   B-B   C-C

Waterline

Scale: 0.5cm = 1m

0 1   5   10

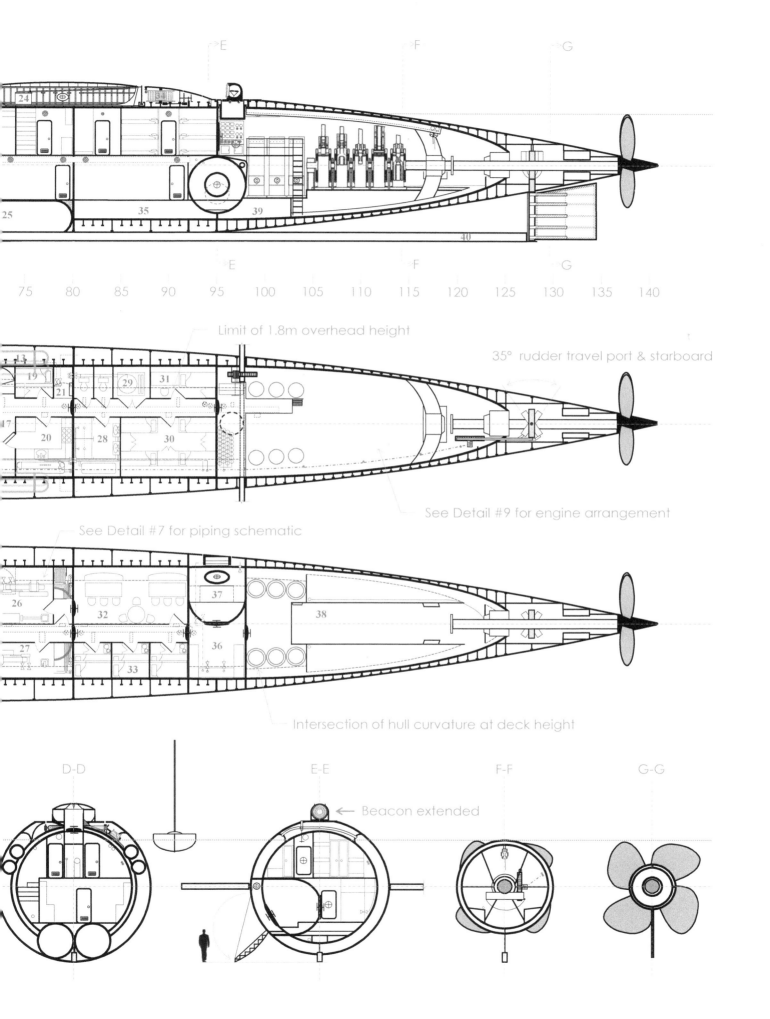

24

34

25

35 39

40

E F G

E F G

75 80 85 90 95 100 105 110 115 120 125 130 135 140

Limit of 1.8m overhead height

35° rudder travel port & starboard

13

19

21

29

31

17

20

28

30

See Detail #9 for engine arrangement

See Detail #7 for piping schematic

26

32

37

38

27

36

33

Intersection of hull curvature at deck height

D-D E-E F-F G-G

Beacon extended

LEGEND

1 – Ram

2 – Forward air reservoir

3 – Forward equipment space (recirculation fans & HP air piping)

4 – Professor Aronnax's cabin

5 – Captain Nemo's cabin

6 – Forward passageway

7 – Forward trim tank

8 – Salon—viewport shutters shown retracted (open)

9 – Battery (198 cells)

10 – Upper equipment space (ship's service air reservoir)

11 – Pilothouse (shown extended)

12 – Library

13 – Main air reservoir (port and starboard, 4 flasks total)

14 – Mate's cabin

15 – Captain Nemo's sea cabin

16 – Air handling room (air compressor & ventilation fans)

17 – Gangway to main hatch

18 – Ship's storeroom

19 – Cook's cabin (used by Ned Land & Conseil)

20 – Galley (fresh water distillation unit outboard)

21 – Access ladder to the dinghy/piping & wiring trunk

22 – Central stair

23 – Dining room

24 – Dinghy (with stowage cover installed)

25 – Main compensation tank (auxiliary trim tank)

26 – Starboard pump room & machine shop

27 – Port pump room

28 – Head (hot water heater outboard)

29 – Ship's laundry

30 – Crew's bunkroom

31 – Chief engineer's cabin

32 – Crew's mess (used as a holding cell)

33 – Crew's cabins (x3)

34 – Electric lantern (shown extended)—retraction cavity below

35 – Potable water tanks 1 & 2, waste tank (starboard side)

36 – Diving dressing room (stowage lockers below deck)

37 – Diving chamber

38 – Engine room

39 – Aft trim tank

40 – Keel

SYMBOLS

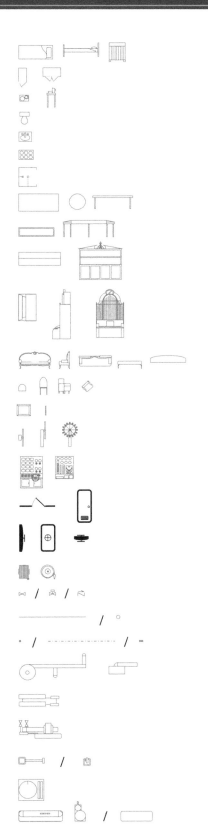

Bed/bunk

Wardrobe

Washstand
Toilet
Sink
Stove
Shower

Table/desk

Display case

Sideboard cabinet

Pipe organ

Couch/divan/bench

Chairs

Picture frame

Ship's helm

Electrical control panel
Ship's instrument panel

Door

Watertight hatch

Fire hose reel

Isolation valve/reduction valve/check valve

Piping (schematic)/cross section representation

Pulley/rudder cables/cross section representation

Ventilation blower and ductwork

Air compressor

Water pump

Lathe/drill press

Washing machine

Freshwater still/hot water heater

Examples of late
19th century machinery

Air compressor

Motor-driven pump

Ventilation blower

Electric motor

Submarine Development

Despite modestly successful demonstrations in 1800, Robert Fulton was unable to sell his submarine boat to either France or England and his improved designs were never built. He was followed by Brutus de Villeroi, an engineer and professor in Nantes, France, who conducted submerged experiments with a three man submarine in 1832. Twenty-five years later in the United States, he built a larger submarine for the purpose of conducting salvage. Reports of its success led the U.S. Navy to contract him to construct the submarine that would become known as the Alligator. Though promising, it proved ineffective at clearing the James River and was subsequently lost off Cape Hatteras while under tow in a storm.

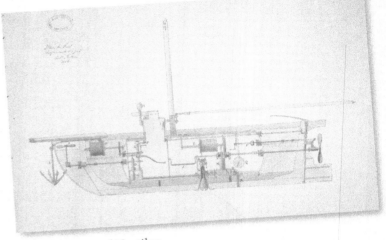

Fulton's improved Nautilus

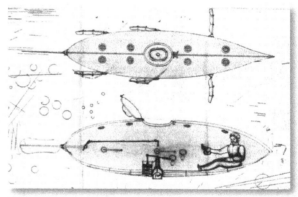

Villeroi's 1832 submersible

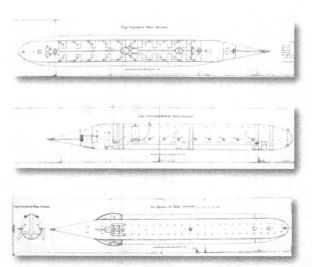

Alligator

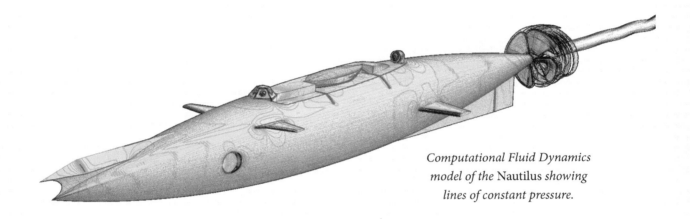

Computational Fluid Dynamics model of the Nautilus *showing lines of constant pressure.*

Design Engineering

NOTES TO ACCOMPANY THE DRAWINGS

These drawings of the *Nautilus* are intended to adhere strictly to the description provided in the text. In those instances where the text provides latitude in interpreting the design, our staff has endeavored to incorporate realistic modern submarine design practices to the greatest extent possible. We have kept such design influences consistent with the technology of the period advanced to the degree suggested by Professor Aronnax's description. This blend of strict compliance with specifics as related in the Professor's memoir, coupled with modern submarine design wherever possible, we feel has resulted in the most accurate and realistic depiction of the *Nautilus* to date. In a very few instances where we have stretched our interpretation of the text or departed from traditional interpretations in order to satisfy essential engineering practice, we have carefully documented the extent of the deviation. In addition, some features and systems have been included that would be required for proper operation of a vessel such as the *Nautilus,* but are not specifically referenced in the text.

Figure 1: The Nautilus

Nonetheless, there are some characteristics which simply cannot be reconciled, even against all the advances in technology to date. The first of these is the extreme depth capability of the *Nautilus* as reported in their dive to the bottom of the ocean identified (incorrectly) as 16,000 meters. Even allowing for modern materials, advanced welding techniques, and optimized design, such a depth rating appears simply beyond the capability of Captain Nemo's design. However, if we are willing to disregard the occasional extreme depth excursion, then the majority of depths actually recorded throughout their travels in the *Nautilus* are certainly within the realm of possibility. The second feature that presents considerable mystery is Captain Nemo's source of electrical power. Assuming Captain Nemo is not engaged in deception, he describes his power source as a metallic sodium, sulfuric acid, primary battery. Although this chemistry can produce an energetic reaction, a battery capable of providing the power for the voyage described simply could not be made to fit inside the *Nautilus*. Even if we assume Captain Nemo has developed much more powerful modern molten sodium cells, the energy density is simply insufficient. In addition, the propulsion mechanism described to convert this electrical power into the necessary shaft horsepower required to achieve a stated speed of 50 mph seems highly suspect. This is examined in greater detail later in the notes, however taken together, we are unable to propose a credible technology for Captain Nemo's power source.

Professor Aronnax's memoir of his *Nautilus* adventure, entitled *Twenty Thousand Leagues Under the Sea,* was originally published in chapters as a magazine serial. In 1871 when the first compilation of the entire tale was published in book form, it included many woodcut illustrations. While generally faithful to the text, inconsistencies are apparent among the different depictions. The artists responsible for these original illustrations, Alphonse de Neuville and Édouard Riou, were collaborators of the author and his publisher Hetzel, thus, although they should not be regarded as definitive, they are at least representative of the author's vision and intent. For that reason they are included within the notes, and the insight they provide is incorporated into these design drawings to the extent that it either does not conflict with the text, or with necessary submarine design practice.[1] Indeed, it has been our ambition that the reader is able to visualize within these plans the scenes as they are depicted in the woodcut illustrations. All quotations from the text that appear throughout these notes are taken from the following edition, which is considered the definitive English translation: Verne, Jules, *20,000 Leagues Under the Sea*, Naval Institute Press, Annapolis, MD, 1993.

Figure 2: Winans' Cigar Ship

EXTERNAL HULL FORM

"'It is a very long cylinder with conical ends. In shape it very much resembles your cigar, a shape already used in London in several vessels of the same sort. From end to end, the cylinder is exactly 70 meters long, and its beam, at its widest point, is eight meters.'" p. 84

"The bow and stern of the *Nautilus* formed that spindle shape that properly caused it to be compared to a long cigar." p. 91

A key insight into the shape of the *Nautilus* is provided by Michael Crisafulli,[2] who has connected the reference to "a shape already used in London" with ships that were designed and built by the Winans family between 1858 and 1866. Their radical marine design concept (figure 2) included an ultra-streamlined spindle-shaped hull with minimum superstructure and were commonly referred to as "cigar ships." At least four ships were constructed and two of these attracted considerable public attention, as well as skepticism and outright criticism from the technical establishment. Their final ship was launched in 1866 in London, while Verne was drafting the story. The *Ross Winans* was 256 ft long, had a 16 ft diameter and displaced about 400 tons.[3] The Winans' hull patent provides the geometric construction for its spindle shape as two intersecting circular arcs symmetrically revolved to produce a circular cross section.[4] For the *Nautilus*, whose hull diameter is 8 m and length is 70 m, the intersecting arcs have a radius = 155.125 m. This shape, shown in blue in figure 4a, represents the outer, or non-pressure, hull. From the volume of this shape, the prismatic coefficient, a measure of how quickly the cross section area changes, can be calculated to be 0.54.[5] This low value is very near an optimum of 0.6 and is indicative of fine versus full ends, suggesting a boat that will slip through water easier and encounter less wave-making resistance.[6] In selecting a cigar ship form, Verne has chosen a very narrow profile to reduce the effect of pressure drag, also called form drag, upon his submerged hull form.

"'And so it isn't altogether constructed on the ten-to-one ratio like your fast ships, but its lines are sufficiently long, and the curves sufficiently gradual, so that the displaced water is easily moved aside and acts as no obstacle.'" p. 84

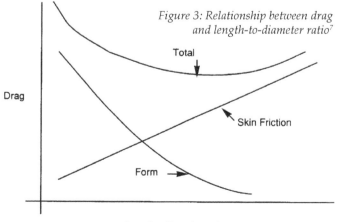

Figure 3: Relationship between drag and length-to-diameter ratio[7]

Drag

Total

Skin Friction

Form

Length : diameter ratio

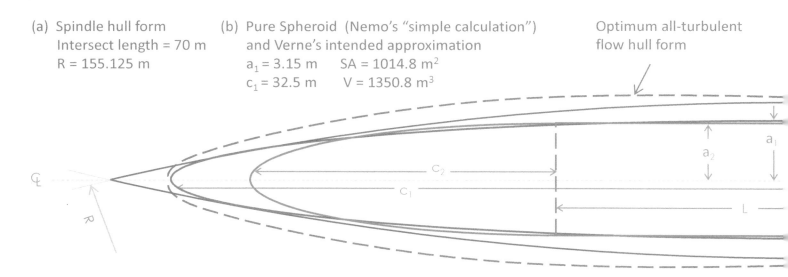

(a) Spindle hull form
Intersect length = 70 m
R = 155.125 m

(b) Pure Spheroid (Nemo's "simple calculation")
and Verne's intended approximation
a_1 = 3.15 m   SA = 1014.8 m^2
c_1 = 32.5 m   V = 1350.8 m^3

Optimum all-turbulent
flow hull form

However, there is a second form of drag, known as skin friction drag, which results from the viscous shear drag of water flowing tangentially over the surface of the hull. This drag increases with surface area and roughness. Thus an optimized design seeks to reduce the surface area as much as possible for a given hull volume while avoiding roughness and sharp discontinuities. The combined minimum of these two performance curves, shown in figure 3, produces an optimal length-to-diameter ratio of approximately 7.7:1, where total drag is a minimum. In this regard, the design of the *Nautilus* fares quite well at 8.75:1 against modern submarines, which tend to vary between 8:1 and 12:1.

The *Nautilus* also exhibits elements of an ideal all-turbulent hull form; all-turbulent because from a practical standpoint, laminar flow is not achievable in a real-world ocean medium. This ideal hull is usually described as an elliptic bow and parabolic stern, which results in a continuously changing diameter along the whole length. Although in the *Nautilus*, the maximum diameter is set amidships rather than an optimal 35-40% back from the bow. Such an ideal teardrop shape was experimentally used on the U.S. Navy submarine *Albacore*, and later incorporated into the *Skipjack* class early nuclear submarine. Although exceptionally fast, the constantly changing cross section demanded by the teardrop shape is expensive and difficult

to build and complicates internal arrangements. As a result, the cylinder with conical tapered aft section and a rounded bow has become the standard shape for U.S. submarines. Since the *Nautilus* does not need to accommodate hydrophones or torpedo tubes in the bow, and moreover, since Captain Nemo intends to ram surface vessels, the narrow front aspect (low prismatic coefficient) is entirely appropriate. A low prismatic coefficient (or fine end) forward promotes motion stability, while aft it contributes to propulsive efficiency. The benefit of lacking a sail, which contributes up to 30% of the drag in typical submarines, is somewhat offset by the presence of the ram.[8] The ram, together with the keel and rudder, create asymmetry about the horizontal plane. The drag from the ram would be expected to produce an upward pitching moment and the keel a downward pitching moment during forward motion. Possibly these could be made to offset each other through careful design, however the many subtle and unpredictable influences of the fluid medium through which the vessel travels is likely to make longitudinal stability elusive. This drives the need for a highly responsive means of providing a counteracting moment. Trim ballast systems have historically proven to be too unresponsive to effectively neutralize longitudinally destabilizing forces, thus control planes are required; the location and operation of which will be described later.

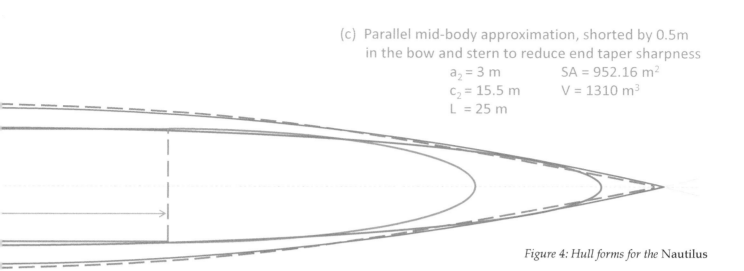

(c) Parallel mid-body approximation, shorted by 0.5m
in the bow and stern to reduce end taper sharpness

$a_2 = 3$ m   SA = 952.16 m^2
$c_2 = 15.5$ m   V = 1310 m^3
L = 25 m

Figure 4: Hull forms for the Nautilus

PRESSURE HULL FORM

"'Now the *Nautilus* has two hulls, one interior, one exterior...'" p. 84

The volume of a spindle the size and shape of *Nautilus's* outer hull is 1,883.6 m^3. This volume is known as the envelope displacement. At first glance, this number seems to contradict the value given by Captain Nemo:

"'These two dimensions give you, via a simple calculation, the surface area and volume of the *Nautilus*. The area comprises 1,011.45 square meters, its volume 1,507.2 cubic meters, which is to say that when entirely submerged, it displaces 1,500 cubic meters of water, or weighs 1,500 metric tons.'" p. 84

The narrative disregards the difference in density between pure water (1 m^3 = 1,000 kg) and seawater which is, on average, 1.025 times heavier. Since the *Nautilus* is intended to operate in the ocean, its volume will actually displace 1,544.88 t of seawater, which must be accounted for by ensuring there is sufficient main ballast margin, otherwise the ship will be unable to submerge. With regard to our consideration of pressure hull form, it is important to note that Captain Nemo says "volume" of the *Nautilus* but then quick-

ly qualifies it as submerged displacement, which is distinctly different than envelope displacement if the spindle-shaped outer hull incorporates free flooding space. This suggests that the discussion has moved from the external hull to the pressure hull. The lack of clarity in their dialogue can be explained by the fact that with the blueprints spread before them, what they are referencing would be obvious.

"The Captain placed before me a drawing that gave the floor plan, cross section, and side view of the *Nautilus*. He began his explanation..." p. 84

However, what is clear is that this total volume includes the volume of the main ballast tanks needed to submerge.

"'So,' the captain continued, 'when the *Nautilus* is afloat, she does stand one-tenth out of water. And if I design some ballast tanks equal in capacity to that one tenth, tanks able to hold 150.72 metric tons, and if I fill them with water, the boat would now displace 1,506.2 metric tons—or weigh that much—and would be completely immersed.'" p. 85

This discussion introduces one of the classical dilemmas of naval architecture: whether to treat the flooded water as added weight in the submarine or lost volume; either way the result is less buoyancy, and sometimes it is convenient to treat it in one way or the other. From their dialogue, it would appear that Captain Nemo regards this as adding weight. Where this ballast tank volume is located has important ramifications for sizing the inner hull. Since main ballast tanks need only be at ambient sea pressure, they are traditionally located between the pressure hull and outer hull. Thus the spindle (exterior) hull must accommodate at least 150 m³ of main ballast volume (actually 155 m³ corrected for seawater) in addition to the pressure (inner) hull, which must therefore have a volume of 1,350 m³.

The shape of the inner hull must be contained within the spindle-shaped outer hull, should have a volume of 1,350 m³ (as we have just derived) and a surface area of 1,011 m² as given by Captain Nemo, and present an optimum shape for resisting sea pressure. A prolate spheroid as depicted in red in figure 4b satisfies these requirements nicely and easily fits the characterization of "cigar shaped" (to an even greater degree than the Winans spindle). It's worth noting that the longitudinal axis of this spheroid (figure 4b) is 65 m long, a number that precisely corresponds to the tally of internal dimensions during Aronnax's tour of the Nautilus. It is our belief that this is the shape Verne used to derive his interior layout.

However, the continuous curve of this shape makes it difficult and expensive to manufacture, and such impracticality has driven modern submarines to adopt a

Figure 5: Reviewing plans of the Nautilus

straight cylindrical mid-section with spheroid or conical end sections. Captain Nemo's earliest description of the hull form as an elongated cylinder with conical ends may suggest he has done the same. The cylindri-

Table 1: The Nautilus Pressure Hull

Space	Values (m)	Volume (m³)	Surface Area (m²)
Cylindrical portion of the pressure hull	r = 3, l = 25	706.8	471.2
Spheroid portion of the pressure hull	a, b = 3, c = 15.5	584.3	466.3
Forward air bank (4 cylinders)	r = 0.35, l = 3.1	5.5	33.4
Amidships air bank (4 cylinders)	r = 0.35, l = 6.7	11	65.1
Compensation tank extension to outer hull (2 half cylinders)	r = 0.925, l = 8.05	25.0	17.0
Dinghy (spheroid approximation)	a = 1.1, b = 0.8, c = 4	14.7	38.5
Dinghy access well (spherical approximation)	r = 0.8	0.6	2.3
Wheelhouse (extended)	r = 1, l = 0.75	4.5	11.0
Reflector light (spherical internal housing)	r = 0.4	Retracts into spheroid hull	
Total enclosed pressure volume (design target = 1,350 m³)		1,352.4	
Total surface area of pressure hull components (design target = 1,011 m²)			1,104.8

cal approximation used in the drawings is shown in green in figure 4c. In taking this practical engineering approach, we have chosen to make the forward air reservoirs separate cylindrical structures outside the pressure hull. Doing so shortens the forward spheroid portion of the hull, which also improves slightly the diameter available in the area of the salon. This is beneficial as the salon is the most challenging space to accommodate, and it places the inner and outer hull in close proximity at a point convenient to locate the salon viewports. For the sake of symmetry, the aft hull spheroid has been similarly shortened, resulting

in a shorter engine room. The justification for this and impact on equipment arrangement is discussed later, however it affords additional space aft of the pressure vessel to accommodate the rudder handling gear. Overall, adopting form 4c has the effect of slightly reducing the surface-area-to-volume ratio from the figures cited by Captain Nemo for the more efficient hull form (figure 4b). A summation of all the pressure-resistant enclosures found in the design, which form the entire pressure envelope responsible for the displaced volume and thus buoyancy of the *Nautilus*, can be found in table 1.

WEIGHT AND BUOYANCY

"'These two hulls are manufactured from steel plates whose relative density is 7.8 times that of water. The inner hull has a thickness of no less than five centimeters and weighs 394.96 metric tons. The second envelope, the outer hull, includes a keel 50 centimeters high and 25 wide, which by itself weighs 62 metric tons; add to this the engine, the ballast, the accessories and accommodations, the bulkheads and interior braces, and we have 961.52 metric tons, which, added to 394.96 gives us the desired total of 1,356.48 metric tons.'" p. 85

"'Now I have supplementary ballast tanks that can ship 100 metric tons of water.'" p. 86

"'I use my supplementary tanks only to reach a depth of 1,500 to 2,000 meters, and that with a view to saving my engines. When I have a mind to visit the ocean depths two or three vertical leagues below the surface, I use slower but equally sure means.'" p. 86

With the basic form and dimensions of the outer and inner hull determined, a ballpark check of the weight figures can be made. Hand calculations, such as Verne would have done, are given here until such time that a detailed 3D engineering model can be completed to provide more precise figures. The outer spindle hull is 2 cm thick producing a weight of 167.2 t. The weight of a prolate spheroid (figure 4b) made of steel with a thickness of 5 cm is 377.5 t; very close to the figure quoted, another sign that this is the correct shape. There are four watertight bulkheads of varying diameters. If we approximate using an average diameter of 6.5 m and a thickness of 5 cm, their weight is 11.2 t each, or 44.8 t. Over the cylindrical portion of the pressure hull, stiffening rings have been placed at 0.5 m intervals that are also 5 cm thick and extend 0.25 m beyond the pressure hull. Each of these forty-seven rings weighs 2 t for a total of 94 t. Over the spheroid part of the pressure hull, these rings remain at 0.5 m intervals, however they extend to the outer hull. Since the hull tapers to a point,

the diameter of these sixty rings (thirty on each end) is constantly decreasing from 7.15 m to 3.3 m. Since the space between the inner and outer hulls varies with the curvature of the spheroid shell, the width of each ring is also constantly changing. Additionally, this entire volume is a free flood space, thus there must be lightening holes located in some of the larger rings to allow water to freely flood and drain. As an approximation, a diameter of 5 m, a thickness of 5 cm and a width of 0.5 m gives a weight of about 1.5 t each or a total of 90 t. Together

Figure 6: The Nautilus *on the surface*

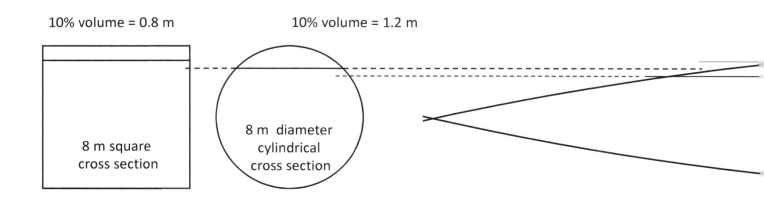

10% volume = 0.8 m   10% volume = 1.2 m

8 m square cross section

8 m diameter cylindrical cross section

these weights are 773.5 t. Our keel is 33.6 m long which produces a volume of 4.2 m³ using the height and width given by Captain Nemo. If this were solid, its weight would be 33 t. This is half of Captain Nemo's number, however, he doesn't mention support for the ram, which is 14.5 m long. At 50 cm wide and 25 cm high, this produces a volume of 1.8 m³, which represents an additional 14 t. Finally the prodigious weight of the salon viewport assemblies must be considered. The shutter assembly at 2.5 t, the glass weighing some 1.5 t and the cast hull insert holding the window which is on the order of 10 t, provide a total of approximately 14 t for each viewport.

These weights total 848.5 t, representing 62.5% of the total, which compares well to modern submarines in which structure, including any permanent ballast, comprises approximately 50% of the total weight. If we consider that the *Nautilus* carries little in the way of payload (i.e. weapons), then the 8-9% of weight this accounts for in modern submarines can be further allocated to structure. Main and auxiliary equipment is typically 35% of total weight, which would give the *Nautilus* a machinery allowance of 474.7 t. Comparison of weight and space allowances for the *Nautilus* versus modern conventional (SSK) and nuclear (SSN) submarines is provided in table 2. For any submarine, the major source of buoyancy (typically >90%) is the volume displaced by the pressure hull. Though the spindle hull has a volume of 1,883.6 m³, the total displacement of the *Nautilus* is given as 1,500 m³. The difference being the free flood and ballast tank volumes outside the pressure hull. Using a value between 90-95% of the displacement for the

contribution of the pressure hull gives a pressure hull volume that correlates nicely with the calculations in table 1, and is consistent with the weight derived in the preceding paragraph. This correlation is a further indication that our geometry and dimension of the inner and outer hulls is correct.

"The platform emerged only 80 centimeters or so, less than three feet, out of water." p. 91

According to Captain Nemo, the main ballast tank volume of 150 m³ represents 10% of the *Nautilus's* displacement, yet on the surface, the *Nautilus* is observed to have 0.8 m of freeboard to the top of the platform. For a square-shaped cross section, 0.8 m of freeboard corresponds to 10% of the hull volume. However if the hull is cylindrical, then volume is concentrated along the longitudinal axis and the freeboard corresponding to 10% of the volume above the waterline is 1.2 m. The spindle shape further concentrates volume axially, thus for 10% of the volume to be above the waterline, there must be 1.6 m of freeboard (figure 7). This suggests that in order for the platform to be anywhere close to 0.8 m above the waterline, it must be formed by truncating the spindle shape rather than constructing a platform tangent to the apex of the outer hull. A narrow superstructure mounted along the center of this platform houses the access hatch, dinghy, and other essential topside equipment. Such a configuration is also consistent with the arrangement demonstrated by *Plongeur* (figure 16), which was surely an important influence. Prediction of an exact freeboard is complicated by a number of factors. The free flood space inside the outer hull makes

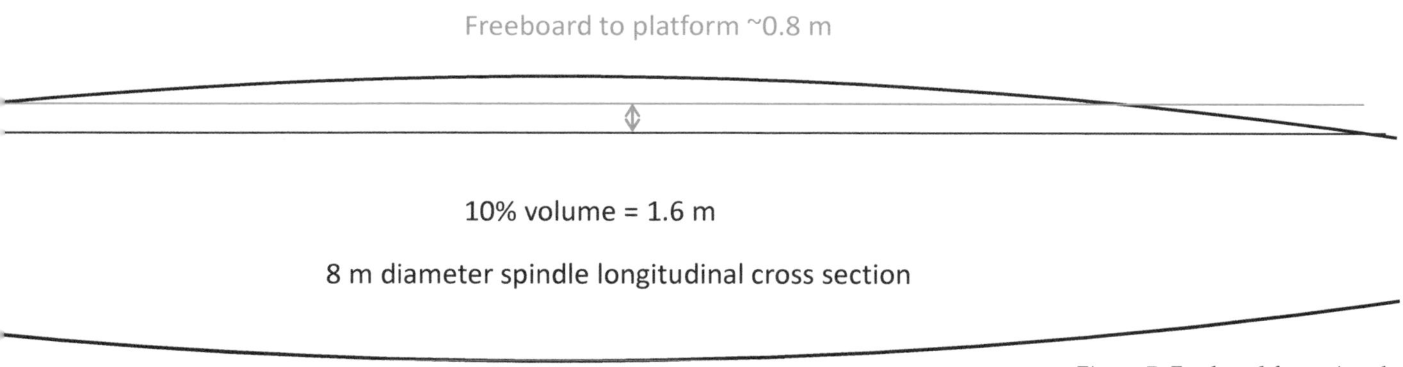

Freeboard to platform ~0.8 m

10% volume = 1.6 m

8 m diameter spindle longitudinal cross section

Figure 7: Freeboard for various hull shapes

the displaced volume somewhat less spindle-shaped, although this effect is small. Additionally, when the *Nautilus* surfaces, the volume of the dinghy and pilothouse are lifted clear of the water, thus their displacement no longer contributes to buoyancy. The loaded condition of the vessel is another, obvious, impact to waterline. Irrespective of these relatively minor variations, 10% reserve buoyancy is a low number, though not unlike other early submarine designs. Mature diesel-electric submarines, which frequented the surface, evolved to a reserve buoyancy of 20-30%, while modern nuclear submarine design has returned to values around 10%.[9] For the *Nautilus*, the resulting low freeboard creates a risk of swamping the main hatch when opened at sea. Consider that a typical Sea State 3 condition, characterized as "slight," represents 0.5-1.25 m wave heights, while a "moderate" Sea State 4 has wave heights up to 2.5 m.[10] In addition to placing the hatch at the highest point on the pressure hull, other measures, described later, have been provided to further mitigate this risk

of flooding. A final consideration, important for all submarines, but especially in those with marginal reserve buoyancy, is avoiding operation with main ballast tanks only partially emptied. This creates a free surface effect within the tank at a time when the submarine is in a condition of instability; with the center of buoyancy and center of gravity located close together such that little righting arm exists to correct a heeling moment (figure 8).

Main ballast tanks are situated in pairs between the inner and outer hull, divided at the keel, and connected by a common vent at their top. Valve handles for manual vent operation extend through the pressure hull at the forward and aft ends of the upper passageway. The tanks outboard of compartment four (frames 80-95) and the after half of compartment two (frames 45-60) have nearly equal volumes that total approximately 190 m³ minus the structure present within. These four saddle tanks represent the *Nautilus's* principal main ballast tanks used for routine sur-

Table 2: Weight and Space Allowances[11]

Component	Typical SSK		Typical SSN		The *Nautilus*	
	Weight %	Space %	Weight %	Space %	Weight %	Space %
Payload	9	28	8	30	0	0
Structures	43	-	45	-	60	-
Main & aux machinery	35	56	35	55	~35	53
Accommodation & outfit	4	11	4	10	~5	46
Stores	1	5	1	5	<1	1
Permanent ballast	8	-	7	-	0	-

facing events to provide 0.8-1.0 m of freeboard. Given the margin of error in the weight approximations presented earlier, the ballast tanks outboard of compartment three can be regarded as an engineering reserve. When emptied, these tanks can provide approximately 150 t of additional buoyancy. Should detailed engineering models demonstrate that these tanks are unnecessary, we might postulate that they serve as Captain Nemo's emergency reserve. To conserve air, they are not routinely utilized, but they provide some redundancy in the event one of the principal main ballast tanks become damaged, provide additional freeboard when surfacing in heavy seas, and double the available buoyancy in the event an emergency surface is required. The air reservoirs, sized to be able to blow 150 m^3 dry at the surface three times, can easily blow the combined volume of 300 m^3 in an emergency. When the *Nautilus* is on the surface, the open flood grates at the bottom of these tanks lie approximately 7 m below the waterline, thus the air pressure inside the tanks required to oppose the entry of water is 1.7 atmospheres. Applying the ideal gas law gives the air reservoir volume (5.1 m^3) necessary to blow the tanks dry. The *Nautilus* has three air reservoirs reserved for ballast tank blow, one in the bow and one port and starboard, amidships between the inner and outer

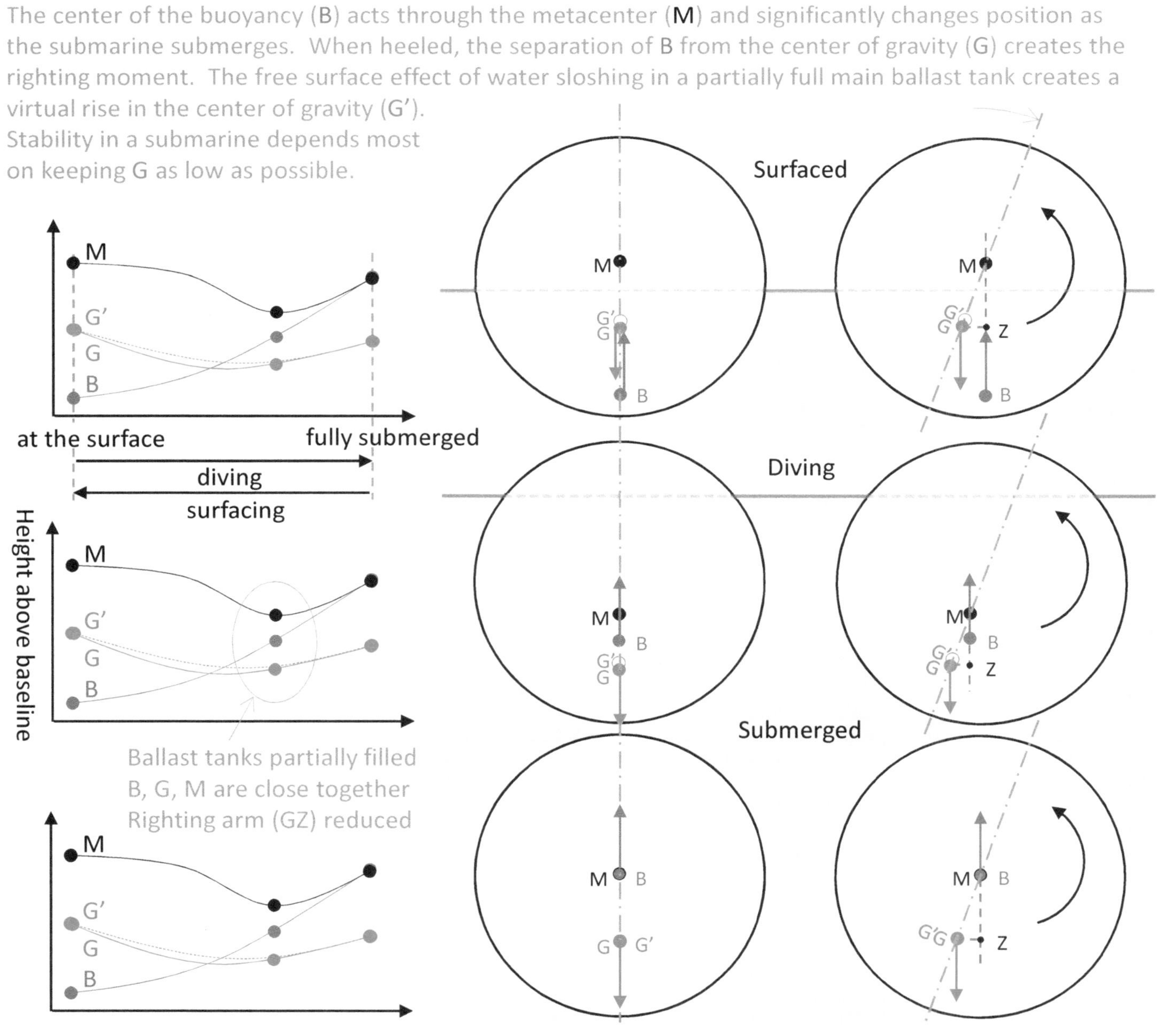
The center of the buoyancy (B) acts through the metacenter (M) and significantly changes position as the submarine submerges. When heeled, the separation of B from the center of gravity (G) creates the righting moment. The free surface effect of water sloshing in a partially full main ballast tank creates a virtual rise in the center of gravity (G').
Stability in a submarine depends most on keeping G as low as possible.
Surfaced
Diving
Submerged
M
G'
G
B
Z
at the surface
fully submerged
diving
surfacing
Height above baseline
Ballast tanks partially filled
B, G, M are close together
Righting arm (GZ) reduced

Figure 8: Submarine stability

hull. A minimum storage pressure of 50 atm is derived from Captain Nemo's statement that the diving apparatus are charged to this pressure. Good submarine design usually provides sufficient high-pressure air

to perform three main ballast tank blows. This would require a total air reservoir volume of 15.3 m³ and the three air banks provided in the design total 16.5 m³.

"The pumps began to expel water from the ballast tanks." p. 91

"The *Nautilus's* powerful pumps were forcing air into the tanks and storing it under high pressure." p. 305

"Our full electric power was applied to the pumps, which began to expel water from the ballast tanks. In a few minutes the pumps had checked our descent." p. 332

"In any event, the *Nautilus* was going to try. I could feel it assuming an oblique position, lowering the stern, raising the ram. The captain had accomplished this maneuver by taking in more water in the tanks astern." p. 333

Variable ballast includes the forward and aft trim tanks and the port and starboard compensation tanks located in the lower section of compartment three. The latter are hard tanks, that is, able to withstand sea pressure, thus they take the form of right circular cylinders with hemispherical ends and they extend all the way to the outer hull. It is water in these tanks that is expelled using pumps mounted above. Captain Nemo cites 100 t as the total capacity of the *Nautilus's* "supplementary ballast tanks," and the design provides for very close to 25 m³ in each trim tank and 25 m³ in each compensation tank, for a total volume of 100 m³ or 100 t (102.5 t using seawater density). Customary practice would be to have these tanks not more than half full to allow for both positive or negative adjustments. Maintaining neutral buoyancy requires the ability to accommodate variation in shipboard loading (stores, freshwater production, etc.) and in the environment (temperature and salinity), as well as the hull compression (volume reduction) effects from pressure at depth. To give some idea of the magnitude of the variation, the *Nautilus* must be able to accommodate up to a 3% change in buoyancy (~45 t) due to salinity, an estimated 0.25 t per degree of temperature change or 100 ft increase in depth, and perhaps as much as 0.3 t per 100 ft of depth due to hull compression.[12] Taken together, the change due to pressure and hull compression results in a net decrease of buoyancy as the submarine dives. This is known as the diving rule, and for the *Nautilus* it is probably about 0.15 t per 100 ft. Thus the use of sup-

plemental tanks down to 2,000 m, as Captain Nemo states, would require the ability to de-ballast approximately 10 additional tonnes.

Finally, it is interesting to note the description provided in *The Mysterious Island* when the settlers come upon the *Nautilus* surfaced in an underground cavern:

"...a long fusiform object floated on the surface of the water... This machine, looking like the body of an enormous cetacea, was 250 feet long, and rose ten to twelve feet above the water."

While the shape and length are consistent within the errors of visual estimation, there is no mistaking a freeboard of ten feet as compared to 80 cm consistently found in Verne's earlier book. It seems safe to assume the estimate cited here is not referenced to the platform deck, but rather to the top of the extended wheelhouse; an actual height of 7.8 ft. Still, to explain the disparity of 2-4 ft we must assume that all main ballast tanks have been blown dry and that the *Nautilus* at this point is very lightly loaded. While the absence of a crew and supplies contributes modestly to this condition, a far more significant effect would result from completely draining the internal variable ballast tanks that would normally be kept approximately half full for trim compensation. Confined to his grotto, it's reasonable to think Captain Nemo might do this to provide additional reserve buoyancy at a time when further voyages are not proximate.

HULL CONSTRUCTION

"'Now, the *Nautilus* has two hulls, one interior, one exterior, and they are joined by iron T-bars, which gives the boat terrific rigidity. Because of this cellular arrangement, it has the resistance of a solid block. The plating can't yield; it's self-adhering and not dependent on its rivets; and the homogeneity of its construction, due to the perfect union of the materials involved, permits it to defy the most violent of seas.'" p. 84-85

"I searched all over the outside for an opening, a panel, a hatch, a manhole. But the iron plates were joined tight and solid with rows and rows of iron rivets." p. 48

"The bow and stern of the *Nautilus* formed that spindle shape that properly caused it to be compared to a long cigar. I noticed that its iron plates, slightly overlapping each other, resembled the scales covering the bodies of large terrestrial reptiles." p. 91

On several occasions it is observed that the outer hull is clearly riveted. This common technology of the period would have been cost effective and easy to repair; perhaps an important consideration when you are in the business of ramming surface ships. Detail #1 illustrates the methods that were employed for affixing hull plating in the period when the *Nautilus* was constructed. Rolling machines at that time were only just being able to form T- and I-beams, and so it is unclear whether the stiffening rings, to which the outer hull plating is attached, would have been rolled as single pieces or built up. The description provided by Professor Aronnax of the outer plating suggests that the "clinker" arrangement (method b) was most likely the one used. One advantage to this method, considering the remote site of assembly, is that it avoids the need to carefully plane the ends of the plate to ensure tight butt joints. Both Lloyd's and Liverpool rules at the time specified double riveting the butts of all outside plating as standard practice. Chain riveting (vice zig-zag riveting) would likely have been preferred as the stronger method.[13] Given the difficulty of sourcing and shipping the hull materials to Captain Nemo's island shipyard, we can assume that the holes for these rivets were drilled on-site, instead of punched at the foundry, to ensure greater accuracy. The drawings depict the outer hull formed of overlapping riveted plates that measure 2 m in width over the midsection and 1.5 m over the rapidly tapering areas forward and aft. Six plates of equal size are used to encircle the circumference, thus their length gradually reduces from a maximum of 4.19 m at the midsection. The use of longer plates tends to make a ship stronger, lighter, and more expensive. Typical plates used were on the order of 1 m x 3 m, although by the end of the century, major shipyards were employing plates as large as 3 m x 10 m. Given Captain Nemo's austere assembly location and the tighter curves found on the *Nautilus*, smaller sizes seem appropriate. A thickness of 2 cm has been chosen, which would not have been uncommon for the protective bottom of traditional double-hulled vessels of the period. A good comparison can be made with CSS *Manassas*, a Confederate steam-propelled ram ship sheathed in 3 cm iron plates which, along with her convex hull projecting just 6.5 ft above the waterline, caused cannon shot to bounce off harmlessly.[14] So too, for the *Nautilus's* hull.

Although steel plate was beginning to be produced in the size and thickness required, its quality and therefore structural qualities were often inconsistent. Thus is it likely that the plates of the outer hull are fabricated from wrought iron, which was still the preferred material for armor applied to warships, as it was less brittle than cast iron and could be hammered and shaped when reheated. However, the understructure that supports the outer hull is almost certainly fashioned from steel, as steel brackets and framing were well established and superior to iron. This outer hull needs only the strength to resist collision with the seas and with ships, as the strength to resist the pressure at depth resides with the inner hull. Captain Nemo describes "a perfect union of materials" that "coheres spontaneously." This was undoubtedly inspired by a demonstration at the 1867 Exposition in Paris in which Henry Wilde used an electric arc-light to fuse iron rods measuring 15 inches long and 1/4 inch in diameter.[15] It appears that Captain Nemo has advanced the "fusion of metals by voltaic electricity" pioneered by J.P. Joule to develop a practical welding process that is much superior to riveting.[16] This would represent significant technical progression, since the first known all-welded vessel, the British ship *Fullagar*, was built in 1920, some fifty-five years after the *Nautilus* was constructed.[17] To achieve any significant depths, the pressure hull would have to be welded. The necessary precision of this task at the scale required for a submarine hull is daunting indeed since as little as 0.5% out-of-roundness can significantly reduce hydrostatic load carrying capacity by 35%.[18] In addition, modern submarine pressure hulls are reinforced with stiffening rings that are typically located inside the pressure hull to reduce the tension felt by the welds. However, an externally stiffened cylinder can be equally effective in resisting pressure. This is a logical configuration in a dual hulled vessel. In the drawings, stiffening rings are placed from stem to stern at half meter intervals. In the narrower free flood portion of the hull, these rings are extended to the outer hull to provide additional strength and rigidity as described by Captain Nemo. In the areas amidships where the main ballast tanks are located, those rings that do not extend to the outer hull project 25 cm from the pressure hull.

SS *Great Britain*, launched in 1843, was the first iron-hulled, screw-propelled vessel to cross an ocean. She had a double bottom and featured five transverse watertight bulkheads, which were a novelty in shipbuilding. Her giant sister ship, SS *Great Eastern*, completed in 1858, had two complete hulls separated by 2'10" of

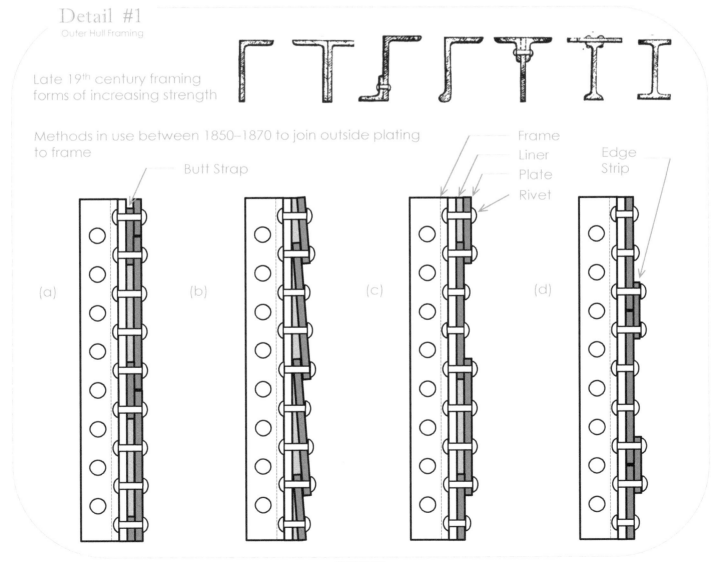

Detail #1
Outer Hull Framing

Late 19th century framing forms of increasing strength

Methods in use between 1850–1870 to join outside plating to frame

Butt Strap

Frame
Liner
Plate
Rivet

Edge Strip

(a)   (b)   (c)   (d)

framing, with plates measuring 27' x 4'3" wide and 1 1/4" thick.[19] Unprecedented in both size and construction technique, Verne no doubt took note of these cutting-edge developments when he traveled to the United States aboard the *Great Eastern* in 1867.[20] For submarines, even more important than assuring compartment integrity in case of flooding, bulkheads provide important stiffening benefits, effectively shortening the length of the shell under stress. However, both bulkheads and section transitions can cause large stress concentrations, even though this influence typically doesn't spread very far into the adjacent structure. The stress concentrations occur because of differences in the radial stiffness of adjacent sections, and the resultant bending of the plating to accommodate the different deflections under external pressure. In the *Nautilus*, the section transition stress is considerably less significant than the bulkhead stress because the geometry change from cylinder to spheroid is quite gradual.

A typical modern practice for the spacing of internal watertight bulkheads is at a distance approximately two hull diameters apart. With the exception of the salon, Captain Nemo has largely adhered to this design practice and taken into account functional and safety considerations as well. As would be expected, a bulkhead is located just forward of the engine room, which is a very large space with several hull penetrations including the propulsion shaft, rudder and stern planes actuators, and the aft access hull plug. This bulkhead also marks the point of transition from a cylinder to spheroid hull form. This bulkhead joins the midline of a transverse cylinder that spans the hull. This watertight structure is so constructed in order to provide both rigidity to the pressure hull and contain the pressure internal to the diving cell when the large egress hatch is open to the sea. The cylindrical compartment is further divided by a hemispherical end cap that provides the strongest enclosure geometry for the diving cell. Finally, this cylindrical bulkhead also provides support for the stern plane axle and counteracts the force generated by deflecting the planes. Bulkheads at either end of compartment three isolate five large penetrations in the pressure hull found in this section, namely the main and dinghy access hatches, the air induction valve, and the two seawater pump suction/discharge valves. Smaller penetrations in compartments three and four

include the trunk cavity drains, waste discharge valve, main ballast vent actuators, and the high-pressure air piping to the outboard reservoirs. The circularity of the pressure hull in the lower part of compartment three is interrupted by two variable ballast tanks. The shape of these tanks (cylindrical with hemispherical ends) ensures they are optimized to resist sea pressure when equalized at depth, and are positioned so that the compressive force of the pressure hull acts through their midline. The tanks are further supported and protected by the keel, which runs forward between them and terminates at the bulkhead forming the forward end of compartment three. Space is reserved between the keel and the variable ballast tanks for the addition of fixed lead ballast, which may be required to adjust the trim of the design and keep the center of gravity low. The final two bulkheads are positioned forward of the salon and aft of the library, thus encompassing the largest open space in the ship. Penetrations within this space include two large viewing windows, the forward planes actuator, forward access hull plug, and the extendable wheelhouse structure. The forward salon bulkhead presents an exception in that it is not located at the forward transition from cylinder to spheroid hull segments (which would bisect the salon). For all of these bulkheads, the number and placement of watertight doors has been carefully considered. Since they are heavy, expensive, and most importantly, represent potential failure points in a watertight bulkhead, conscious effort has been made to limit the number of such penetrations in each of the bulkheads and avoid their placement in close proximity to each other.

For a modern submarine engineer, the standard used for safe design is the American Society of Mechanical Engineers Safety Standard for Pressure Vessels for Human Occupancy (ASME PVHO-1). It has been accepted by the U.S. Coast Guard and U.S. Navy for all pressure vessels under their jurisdiction, and Section 2 of the Standard, which addresses viewport design, has been accepted by the American Bureau of Shipping, Lloyd's Register, and other foreign classification societies. The scope of the design guidance that applies to Captain Nemo's *Nautilus* includes the shell of revolution (pressure hull), the access ports (hatches), viewports (windows), and mechanical penetrators (pipes, shafts, and electrical cables). In addition to basic design, the Standard specifies materials, fabrication techniques, and mounting arrangements. Obviously these standards, and even the materials and processes they prescribe, were not developed in the time of the *Nautilus*, but it is interesting to compare and see how well fiction foreshadows fact. For example, the Standard specifies a pressure hull thickness of greater than 10 mm but not more than 50 mm (the inner hull of the *Nautilus* is a robust 50 mm thick), and an outside-diameter-to-thickness ratio of less than 1,000 (the figure for the *Nautilus* is a conservative 160). Where it does not require too great a departure from the text, we have applied PVHO-1 to the maximum extent practical. Thus "T-bars" become stiffening rings and "oblong" salon windows become circular. Captain Nemo also expresses concern over lingering in the vicinity of extremely hot hydrothermal vents and at extreme

depths, reflecting a respect for material ductility limits and fatigue failure described in the Standard. Modern pressure vessels, and especially viewports, are also given a service life based on time in service and the number of pressure cycles. Since the *Nautilus* is only three years old at the time of Professor Aronnax's account, failures that accrue with age have yet to appear. The design presented here reflects maximum conformance with the Standard and other submarine design best practices. If we assess the design assuming a degree of quality and construction sophistication that existed in the mid-20th century when submarines of the *Nautilus's* scale were actually in production, then the true depth rating of her hull may be reasonably estimated as perhaps 100 m, which is comparable to fleet submarines prior to the advent of high-tensile steels in World War II.

HULL COATING

During the course of the 19th century, as iron ships rapidly displaced wooden-hulled vessels, the challenges associated with corrosion and fouling became acute. As continues to be the practice today, paint and sacrificial anodes made of zinc provide some measure of protection against corrosion. It can be presumed that bars of zinc would be liberally attached throughout all the free flood spaces within the *Nautilus's* external hull. Attempts were made during this period to sheath the external hulls of ships with sheets of zinc. However, in practice, the zinc became too brittle and wasted away too quickly to be of real value, and so this protection scheme is not depicted for the *Nautilus*.[21] The challenge posed by fouling is considerably more daunting. Once kept in check by copper sheathing the wooden hulls of sailing ships, fouling of iron hulls by marine organisms became such a detriment to their speed and handling that it threatened to negate the advantages of all-metal construction. Copper cladding was not an option, as the dissimilar metals set up a galvanic corrosion that accelerated the deterioration of the hull. By the middle of the 19th century, hundreds of patents had been issued for every type of hull coating imaginable, most of which were wholly ineffective.[22] Around the time of the *Nautilus's* construction, the most promising of these coatings was

a brand of so-called plastic paints known as Moravian. They were developed in Trieste, Italy and utilized a proprietary formula of rosin impregnated with a copper material. Of the various formulations, the Moravian green paint, which had to be applied hot (~300°F) in a thickness between 1/20" and 1/32", was found to be the most effective. This was confirmed by extensive U.S. Navy tests at the turn of the century, and although the exact formulation could not be duplicated, this and similar technologies were used well into the 20th century.[23] Despite being expensive, heavy (~2 lbs/yd²), and laborious to apply, it seems likely that Captain Nemo would have employed the best available technology to inhibit corrosion and fouling. Thus the exterior iron hull of the *Nautilus* is likely painted and then coated with a Moravian hot plastic process. The alternative in common use at the time would have been a shellac, doped with copper or mercury compounds, although such formulations proved less durable and less effective in practice.

The resulting appearance is interesting to consider. In two separate instances, Verne utilized the word "noirâtre," which is translated as "blackish," to describe the exterior color of the *Nautilus*. This suggests a very dark, but somewhat indeterminate color. Assuming the underlying paint is black, either a shellac or a hot plastic coating would add a depth to the color and modify the tint to anything from amber to blue to green. This coloration and the unusual surface texture would likely contribute to the *Nautilus* being mistaken for a living animal. It could also be what Professor Aronnax is alluding to when he first describes the hull surface after landing on it.

> "The blackish back on which I was sitting was glossy and smooth, with nothing like overlapping scales. When I kicked it, it gave off a metallic sonority. Incredible as this sounds, it seemed made of bolted plates." p. 47

This is not a contradiction of observation, but rather a gradual expansion of his understanding as he explores the surface he is sitting on in the dark. A hot plastic coating might protect the hull from corrosion and inhibit significant fouling for perhaps as long as eighteen months. The *Nautilus* seems to frequently transit at high speeds and submerged to moderate depths, both of which would further inhibit fouling. Nonetheless, at some point the need to clean and preserve the hull would become inescapable. When and where Captain Nemo performs such maintenance is unknown, as typically, the task requires dry-docking. During the three years the *Nautilus* has been at sea, there are two periods of six months in which no sightings are recorded (see table 3). Perhaps a hull cleaning was accomplished during these times. As an alternative to dry-docking, perhaps it was done waterborne by the crew wearing their diving suits, though admittedly, such an approach precludes the re-application of hot plastic paint. However it is accomplished, the parts of the hull visible to Professor Aronnax appear throughout the voyage to remain clear of fouling and rust, at least to such an extent that it does not merit comment. The only suggestion of the presence of fouling is that under the extreme emergency of escaping suffocation in the ice bank, the top speed achieved is 40 mph (35 kts) despite Captain Nemo having previously stated his top speed as 50 mph (43 kts). At that point in the voyage, the *Nautilus* has been at sea continuously for at least six months, a substantial portion of which has been in tropical waters, and perhaps this is an indication of the presence of fouling beginning to impact performance. If so, a 20% degradation in top speed would not be atypical.

VIEWPORTS

> "Suddenly, through two oblong openings light broke into each side of the salon. The liquid medium outside was vividly lit up by the electric beacon atop the *Nautilus*. Two glass panels separated us from the sea…copper frames held them in place with seemingly infinite strength." p. 95

> "Suddenly there was daylight in the salon, the sheet-iron panels slid shut, and the enchanting vision vanished." p. 100

> "…he [Captain Nemo] ordered the panels be opened…" p. 235

The pressure envelope of the *Nautilus* incorporates seven windows. There are four biconvex viewports mounted in the pressure hemisphere of the pilothouse. Each is set in a reinforced pocket that fills the space between the inner pressure hull and pentagonal outer shell. An outer retaining ring is secured by bolts that pass through all three layers (see detail #4a). The Fresnel lens of the electric beacon is ground onto the outer surface of a conical frustum window that is mounted in a reinforced seat that forms an access hatch for maintenance (see detail #3). Finally, there are the two primary viewing portals located in the second compartment. The giant viewports of the salon are among the most distinctive features of the *Nautilus*, and the perspective they offer is rivaled only by modern submersibles whose pressure vessel is formed from a transparent acrylic sphere. However, within the realm of large submarines, they are unique. Despite their prominence in the story, few actual details of the viewports or their operation are

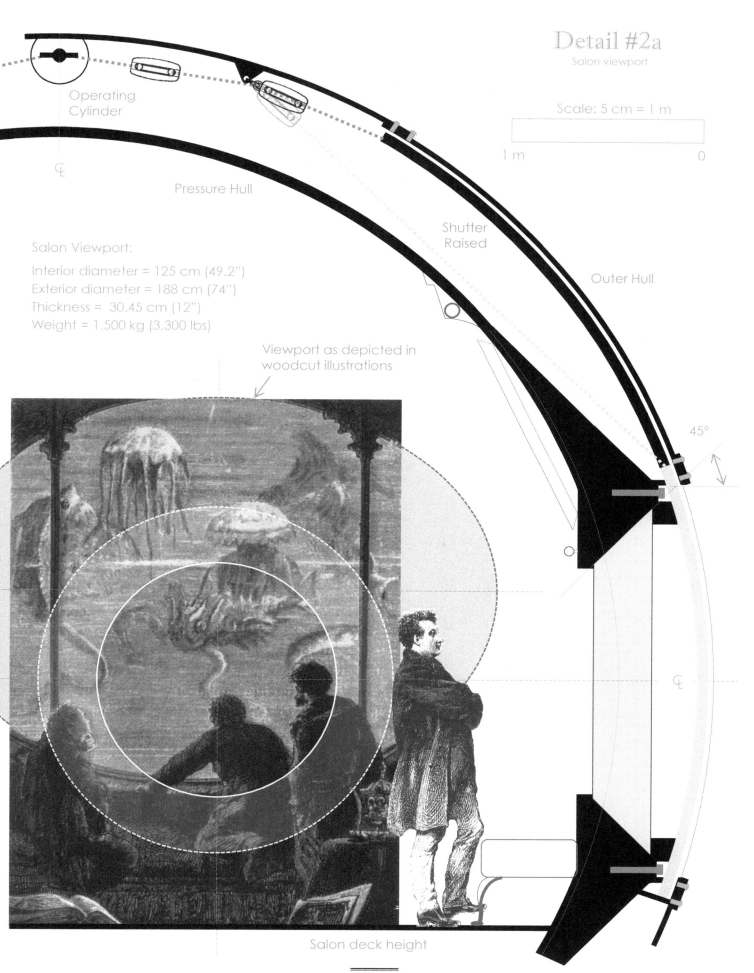

Operating
Cylinder

Pressure Hull

Scale: 5 cm = 1 m

1 m   0

Shutter
Raised

Outer Hull

Salon Viewport:

Interior diameter = 125 cm (49.2")
Exterior diameter = 188 cm (74")
Thickness = 30.45 cm (12")
Weight = 1,500 kg (3,300 lbs)

45°

Viewport as depicted in
woodcut illustrations

Salon deck height

provided. They are depicted with notable consistency in several of the original illustrations as oval in shape, and by comparison with the figures standing in front of them, their measure can be estimated at 2 m high by 3 m wide; dimensions that present considerable challenge to a practical design. To improve stress considerations in the hull and the ability of the viewports to resist pressure, we have chosen to make the viewport circular in shape. However, this is centered on an oval opening in the outer hull to retain the flavor of Verne's design. Despite his obvious genius as an electrochemist, it seems unlikely that Captain Nemo could have also innovated workable acrylics nearly 100 years in advance of their public development, and so we must assume that the viewports are fabricated from glass. This puts us in unexplored design regimes since virtually all modern submarine and submersible construction uses acrylic where transparency is desired.[24] A notable exception is the bathysphere developed by William Beebe and Otis Barton, which descended to a depth of 3,028 ft

in 1934—before the advent of acrylic—and therefore incorporated fused quartz viewports.[25] Fused quartz is glass consisting of silica in non-crystalline form and containing no other ingredients, which are often added to lower the melting temperature. It has superior optical properties and an extremely low coefficient of thermal expansion so it is able to endure large, rapid temperature changes without cracking. It was first produced in 1839, but it was not until 1900 that manufacturing techniques had advanced sufficiently to permit useful fabrication. Interestingly, one of the early applications of fused quartz was to form a transparent housing for a high-pressure mercury arc lamp not unlike the *Nautilus's* beacon.[26]

Although acrylic is the basis for the guidance found in PVHO-1, the underlying design principles of that standard have been applied here. Thus the glass itself is shaped as a 90° conical frustum that presents a trapezoidal cross section with an interior diameter of 1.25 m and a resulting exterior diameter of 1.88 m. This design strikes a balance between challenging-but-feasible engineering, and the desire to capture the expansive field of view described. A thickness of 30 cm is adequate for operations limited to the depth constraints imposed by the hull construction, with a reasonable margin of safety. This is an important consideration since the failure mechanism of glass is quite unlike acrylic. The viewport is set within a thickened portion of the pressure hull, a cast piece welded into the hull, and secured by a bolted retaining ring that forms the backstop for the shutter. The copper that Professor Aronnax observes surrounding the viewports is likely not structural and is possibly a biocide measure to help keep the glass free of bio-fouling. The protective shutters are raised by the extension of an air-operated piston which is controlled from the pilothouse. This explains the lack of observable control in the salon and the need to order them open. The 15 cm bore and 2.4 m stroke of the piston is sized to provide sufficient force to lift the shutters even if the air banks are at half their nominal 50 atm pressure, and while working against sea pressure at a depth of 150 m. When the piston is vented to the space above the library, gravity returns the shutters to the shut position.

Detail #2b
Viewport calculation

Simplified viewport thickness calculation

Required thickness of a uniformly loaded circular glass window is given by:

$$(T) = D\sqrt{(SF)(K)/4} * \sqrt{(P/F_a)} = 36.9 \text{ cm}$$

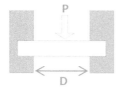

Where:

Safety Factor (SF) = 3

K is an empirically derived value of 0.75 which is suitable for most optical crystals when the perimeter is clamped

Apparent Elastic Limit of Rupture Modulus (F_a) = 1,500 PSI

(this value is conservative, as modern manufactured glass is nominally 10,000+ PSI)

Pressure loading (P) = 233 PSI (150 m depth)

Unsupported diameter (D) = 1.25 m

CONTROL SURFACES AND PROPELLER

"To steer this boat to starboard or to port—that is, to turn on a horizontal plane—I use an ordinary wide-bladed rudder attached to the rear of the stern-post and operated by a wheel-and-tackle. But I can also make the *Nautilus* descend or ascend, on a vertical plane, by slanting its two fins. These are attached to the sides at the center of flotation. They can move in any direction and they're worked from inside by means of powerful levers. If the fins are kept parallel with the boat, it moves horizontally, if they are slanted, the *Nautilus* follows the angle of the slant and, under the thrust of the propeller, either descends on a diagonal as steep as I decide or ascends diagonally. And if I want to rise very rapidly to the surface, I disengage the propeller, and the pressure of the water causes the *Nautilus* to rise vertically, like a balloon filled with hydrogen going up in the air." p. 86

"Captain Nemo decided to make for the ocean floor by diving on an appropriate diagonal: he set his side fins at a 45° angle to the *Nautilus's* waterline. Then he brought the propeller up to its top speed, its fourfold blade churning the waves with indescribable violence." p. 281

"At a signal from the captain, the fins had been set vertically and the propeller disengaged. The *Nautilus* rose with terrific speed, like a balloon shooting into the sky." p. 285

"'The propeller has a diameter of six meters, a pitch of seven and a half meters, and can make 120 revolutions per second.'
'And that gives you?'
'A speed of fifty miles an hour.'" pp. 81-83

"The propeller was beating the water with mathematical regularity, sometimes protruding above the surface and throwing phosphorescent spray to great heights." p. 49

Verne has been unusually precise and rather complete in his description of the arrangement and function of the *Nautilus's* control surfaces. From a hydrodynamic point of view it is desirable to mount the planes at mid-height, level with the axis of the hull, as this maintains symmetric flow over the planes enabling them to be equally effective for rise and dive maneuvers; such planes are also good for maneuvering near and diving from the surface. Unfortunately, their longitudinal placement at the center of buoyancy suffers from an unsophisticated understanding of submarine dynamics. With diving planes located at the center of buoyancy as shown in figure 9, there is no lever arm to affect a pitch moment, thus there can be no rapid adjustment of the submarine's pitch, which could make it difficult to avoid un-

intended depth transients or inadvertent broaching. A forward and aft ballast tank permits static trim adjustment in order to obtain an even keel when submerged, but such systems have historically proven to be insufficiently responsive for dynamic longitudinal control. This compels a difficult deviation from the text. Stern planes, controlled by the engine room watch-stander, are depicted with sufficient lever arm from the center of buoyancy to be effective in setting and maintaining the angle of the ship ordered by the helmsman or for changing depth at higher speeds. For simplicity and to keep them on midline, they have been situated forward of the propulsion shaft; a compromise that is likely to induce the planes-reversal phenomenon (where local force created by the planes dominates the opposing ef-

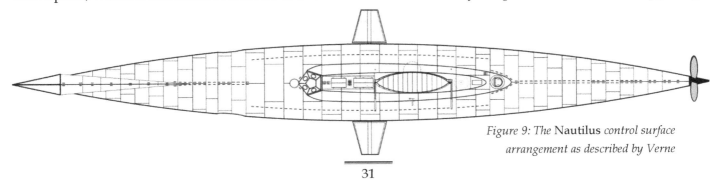

Figure 9: The **Nautilus** *control surface arrangement as described by Verne*

fect of hull pitch attempting to be produced) at higher speeds than if they were located farther aft. Therefore, for depth control at lower speeds, an additional set of planes forward is called for. These smaller planes are controlled directly by the helmsman and have been positioned at the neutral point, approximately one-third of the ship's length back from the bow, where they impart virtually no moment and thus can produce a change in depth without effecting a change in the ship's trim angle. Each are operated through gears and levers acting on a shaft that passes athwartships through the hull supported by structural members that counteract the hydrodynamic forces. To determine the approximate area of each control surface, an experimentally derived thumb rule has been used which is equal to (# of surfaces) x (envelope displacement)$^{2/3}$ x (0.7) or (0.1) or (0.03) for the rudder, stern plane, or bow plane respectively.[27] In order to achieve the best horizontal control effectiveness, the rudder has been situated as far aft as practical. However, considering its low aspect ratio and the control mechanism described, the response to the rudder is likely to be quite sluggish. The principal constraint in sizing the rudder is to prevent damage to it when the Nautilus is bottomed, and in this regard, the keel is configured to provide some protection to the rudder.

Propeller design advanced rapidly, largely through trial and error, from the first six-paddle model installed on SS Great Britain in 1842 such that by the 1888 launching of SS City of New York it achieved an essentially modern form.[28] Given that rapid development and the nascent state of the underlying theory, it is difficult to be sure of the exact form of the Nautilus's four-bladed propeller. Dividing the pitch by the diameter produces a pitch ratio of 1.25, which lies squarely in what we know today to be the optimal range of 0.8 to 1.8 while suggesting a design bias for higher speed. The large diameter would require enormous torque and favor lower shaft speeds. Therefore it seems almost certain that the stated 120 revolutions-per-second is a typo in the original text for a much more realistic revolutions-per-minute. This is claimed to produce a top speed of 50 mph (43 kts). However, the maximum actually witnessed is 40 mph (35 kts), which is interesting since that reflects what is a real threshold for performance regimes and is more consistent with a pitch ratio of 1.25. Such a screw size and performance is comparable to modern submarines, although nearly all employ propellers with an odd number of blades. It is also indicative of the incredible power required of the Nautilus's engine; posing a notable challenge for the thrust bearing technology of the time. While on the surface, Aronnax observes the screw occasionally breaking the surface and this is consistent with its dimensions and placement on the longitudinal centerline of the submarine where it achieves a near optimal propulsive coefficient. There is no mention of any protective structures around the screw nor any portion of the rudder visible on the upper part of the hull and so the drawings are depicted accordingly.

Figure 10: SS Great Britain *(left) and* SS City of New York *(right) displaying screw development between 1842 and 1888*

Figure 11: HMS Polyphemus, *a purpose-built torpedo ram vessel constructed in the 1870s, featured a ram with an integrated torpedo tube*

THE RAM

"She [*Scotia*] was then drawing 6.7 meters of water…" p. 9

"Within moments they located a hole two meters wide in the ship's bottom." p. 9

"Two and a half meters below her waterline there was a regular gash, in the form of an isosceles triangle. This breach in the iron plates was so perfectly defined, it could not have been done more neatly by a punch." p. 9

"'I [Captain Nemo] was navigating two meters beneath the surface when the collision [with *Scotia*] occurred.'" p. 88

"For several hours the *Nautilus's* ram sliced through those whitish waves. I watched its noiseless gliding over that soapy water as it drifted in those foaming eddies sometimes seen between currents entering and leaving a bay." p. 191

"The *Nautilus* entered that brittle mass like a wedge, splitting it with terrible cracklings. It was an old-fashioned battering ram hurled with infinite power." p. 299

Steam propulsion provided the speed, power, and maneuverability for iron ships to be able to use their hulls as offensive weapons. The striking success of CSS *Virginia's* ramming attack on USS *Cumberland* at the Battle of Hampton Roads in 1862 caused navies around the world to consider the ram as the most effective means of attacking armored ships. This perspective was underscored by the spectacular loss of the Italian flagship *Re D' Italia* when rammed by its Austrian opposite number *Ferdinand Max* in the 1866 Battle of Lissa. From that point forward, the majority of capital ships started to go to sea with rams. Although in practice, rams would sink more friendly ships in accidents than enemy combatants in battle, they remained a principal feature of warship design until the end of the 19th century. By then, the development of torpedoes and breech-loading cannon that could effectively hit ships at several-thousand-yard range rendered the ram obsolete.

The *Nautilus's* armament then, is very much a reflection of 1860s naval thinking when the ram was considered the only effective means to counter the development of ironclad warships.[29] The *Nautilus's* ram has been most commonly depicted as an extension of the bow on the centerline of the *Nautilus*, and the spindle shape of the outer hull makes this a most natural conception. However, a ram in such a location is inconsistent with the description of the effects of *Nautilus's* attack. To produce a gash 2.5 m below the waterline of the *Scotia* when Captain Nemo specifies he was traveling 2 m below the surface requires that the ram be located significantly above the *Nautilus's* centerline. We do not know where on the *Nautilus* the submarine's depth is referenced to (modern submarines measure depth from the keel of the boat), but from Captain Nemo's statement it would appear that the deck of the platform is likely the reference for measure. If so, then the ram must lie approximately a half meter below the platform, plus or minus whatever the accuracy of Captain Nemo's depth measurement is. It is somewhat challenging to integrate a ram in this location, and doing so produces undesirable drag and added weight high in the boat. Nevertheless, the drawing presents the ram in its necessary location—able to hit ships just below their waterline as well as break ice on the surface. The fact that Professor Aronnax is able to observe the ram penetrating the waves while on the surface further suggests it cannot be an extension of the spindle bow, but rather a structure mounted above it. A tapered fairing on the backside of the ram aids the extrication of the *Nautilus* from its target following the attack. Consideration for the vulnerability of the diving planes (not to mention the forward air reservoir) if the bow were used for ramming, provides additional rationale for the ram design as shown. Admittedly, this interpretation produces a profile that departs from the clean tapered bow depicted in some of the woodcut illustrations.

TOPSIDE STRUCTURES

"Near the middle of the platform the dinghy was half buried in the hull, forming a slight bulge. Fore and aft rose two cupolas, of medium height, partly enclosed in thick biconvex glass: one was for the steersman, the other held the brilliant electric beacon that lighted his way." p. 91

"They carried out certain very simple procedures that could be called the *Nautilus's* version of 'clearing the decks for action.' First they lowered the manropes that formed a handrail around the platform. Then they pushed the pilothouse and the beacon housing down into the hull until they were flush with the deck. Now nothing protruded from the long steel surface of this cigar-shaped ship; there was nothing to hamper its maneuvers." p. 377

"Meanwhile, a score of the *Nautilus's* crew…had also mounted the platform. They had come up to take in the nets that had been trailing in our wake during the night… They hauled the nets on board. These were large dragnets like those used for trawling on the Normandy coast. They were like huge pockets held half open by a floating pole and a chain laced through lower meshes. These pockets dragged along the seafloor and collected everything in their path." p. 121

The superstructure, along with the ram fairing, are free-flooding structures provided with numerous openings to allow seawater to enter and air to exit upon diving, and the reverse for surfacing. Similar openings have been included along the outer hull to freely vent the space between the hulls that lies above, and therefore outside, the main ballast tanks. The main ballast vent valves are operated from inside by mechanical linkage to isolate the vent line running from the top of each tank to an exit port set flush in the deck of the platform. At the conclusion of *The Mysterious Island*, Captain Nemo indicates there is a means by which these valves can also be actuated externally, allowing the settlers to depart the submarine and then send it to the bottom for eternity.

Within the superstructure of the platform and the space between it and the pressure hull, lie a number of important features that are not specifically observed within the text, but necessary to enable the functionality described. The pressure hull main egress hatch is situated at the center of the intersection of the longitudinal and transverse planes, and thus represents the position of highest freeboard on the hull. The hatch swings up and aft, opening into a watertight well with clamshell doors flush with the top of the superstructure. The well floods when submerged and can be drained to the ballast system upon surfacing where it helps to keep the hatch from becoming swamped; effectively increasing freeboard by an additional 0.7 m. Forward of the main hatch is a deck hatch that accesses a free flooding lock-

Figure 12: Variations in depicting the Nautilus's *topside structures from the original woodcut illustrations*

er used to stow the ship's fishing nets, and also an extra pilothouse viewport, which would seem a prudent spare. The fishing rig described is a beam trawl, modestly sized to permit deployment by hand, although the handling of "more than a thousand pounds of fish" (p. 122) represents arduous work. Beam trawls, like the one described, were pervasive in the English Channel at the time.[30] Professor Aronnax comments that they were constantly towed in the *Nautilus's* wake, however their use would restrict transit speeds to about 4 kts, so clearly Captain Nemo is more selective in their deployment than Aronnax appreciates. In the deep waters where the *Nautilus* primarily navigates, mid-water vice bottom trawling must be assumed. A large mooring ring is provided at the aft end of the platform to secure the nets. This is likely the ring discovered by Ned Land that keeps them from being swept overboard before they are captured by the *Nautilus's* crew.

The railing stanchions that surround the platform pivot at their base and are stowed flush with the deck. A cable, stowed in the deck locker space, is run through the stanchions to form a handrail. Under the platform, connected to the starboard side of the dinghy, is the dinghy access trunk. Like the pilothouse, it is a cylindrical extension of the pressure hull with a hemispherical cap optimized to resist pressure. Forward and aft of the access trunk are the davit mechanisms, which allow the dinghy to be lowered over the port side of the hull to the waterline (see detail #5). Directly aft of the dinghy is the reel for the telegraph wire that connects the dinghy with the *Nautilus*. It has a flange diameter of 1.5 m, a barrel diameter of 0.5 m, and a drum length of 0.5 m, making it capable of stor-

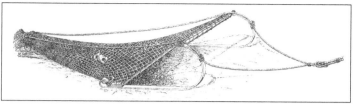

Figure 13: Beam trawl fishing rig

ing 1.5 to 2 km of wire that has a diameter between 2 and 1.5 cm.[31] The generously thick wire is necessary to provide an insulating jacket with enough positive buoyancy to float the wire. An 1858 patent by Charles Oldershaw suggests a means for fabricating such a wire.[32] First, a copper conducting wire is coated with gutta-percha, the natural latex found in trees native to Malaysia that became in high demand mid-century for the purpose of insulating the new trans-Atlantic cables.[33] This wire would then be encased in cork; a diameter of at least 1 cm necessary to provide adequate buoyancy. The outer layer would consist of two tarred fibers, likely manila, braided in opposing spirals to provide protection and tensile strength to the cable. The limited range and significant drag such a cable imposes on the dinghy's mobility suggests that the wire could serve only as a communication connection with a surface buoy, to which the dinghy returns and signals the *Nautilus* for recovery. This concept of operation would accomplish the goal of keeping the *Nautilus* hidden during dinghy excursions, while significantly simplifying the logistics of managing the wire. Rewinding is accomplished manually on the surface after recovering the dinghy by operating a hand wheel, accessible through a hinged panel in the aft end of the superstructure. Aft of the cable reel, the electric beacon can be pushed downward on cables that operate

against the force of lifting springs situated between the hulls. The beacon retracts into a 1.3 m diameter cofferdam that also serves as a hull plug, which can be removed to access the engine room during construction or subsequent maintenance when the *Nautilus* is lightly ballasted and lying in sheltered waters. Another smaller hull plug is located forward of the pilothouse primarily for removing battery cells.

Although seldom used, modern submarines are typically furnished with an anchor, often of the mushroom configuration. No mention is made of an anchor and it would appear that the *Nautilus* is not equipped with a windlass or capstan to retrieve an anchor, handle mooring lines, or assist in the recovery of the trawling nets. The topside superstructure is also unusually devoid of cleats. It's possible that this ubiquitous nautical detail may have been too mundane to warrant observation, or perhaps it is indicative of Captain Nemo's disdain for any attachment to land. Nonetheless, the submarine does moor alongside an "embankment shaped like a wharf" (p. 271) to effect refueling. It should be noted that the projection of the planes would complicate tying this vessel alongside any structure not specifically designed to accommodate it.

ELECTRIC BEACON

"Behind this pilothouse I have placed a powerful electric reflector. Its rays light up the sea for half a mile ahead." p. 88

"One of the *Nautilus's* sailors...came to clean the glass panes around the beacon. I examined the components of that apparatus. It contained biconvex lenses which, as in lighthouses, increased its strength a hundredfold and sent its rays out in the desired direction. That electric apparatus was so constructed as to yield its maximum illuminating power. Its light was produced in a vacuum, ensuring both its steadiness and intensity. The vacuum also reduced wear on the graphite points between which ran the electric arc." p. 184

At the time, carbon arc lamps were just being introduced for public lighting in Paris, and not unreasonably, Professor Aronnax appears to have assumed this technology for the beacon. However, it is unlikely the beacon contains a vacuum, which would be difficult to attain within a pressure housing that must be accessed every few days to replace the electrodes. Furthermore, while it is correct that carbon electrode wear would be reduced in an enclosed environment, in a vacuum there would be no visible arc created since it requires the ionization of some gaseous atmosphere. Thus it is most likely that the carbon arc is initially struck in a standard atmosphere, a fact that has little impact since in short order the vaporization of the carbon produces large quantities of reaction products, including CO and CO_2, which provide the gas for ionization. Rising temperature and pressure, although moderated by submergence in the ocean, would degrade the arc whose intensity would likely fluctuate along with the precipitation of reaction products (soot), which would accumulate and require periodic removal.[34] Potentially this could be done with electrode changes during the *Nautilus's* daily surfacing, however, an apparatus of this sort does seem maintenance intensive and impractical for underwater use. Considering that the Professor is commenting on technology well outside his expertise, invites us to speculate as to what an alternative light gener-

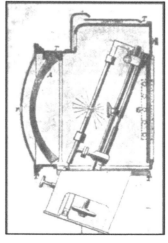

Figure 14: General Electric enclosed carbon arc lamp circa 1911 (left), and a carbon arc searchlight from 1893 (right)

Detail #3
Electric Beacon

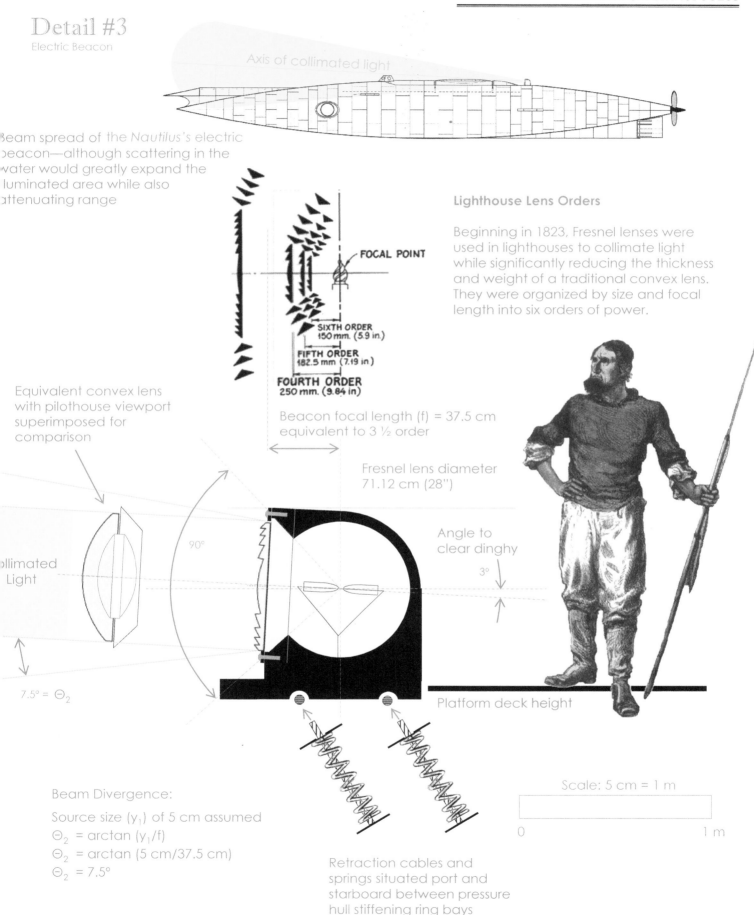

Axis of collimated light

Beam spread of the *Nautilus*'s electric beacon—although scattering in the water would greatly expand the illuminated area while also attenuating range

FOCAL POINT

SIXTH ORDER
150 mm. (5.9 in.)

FIFTH ORDER
182.5 mm (7.19 in.)

FOURTH ORDER
250 mm. (9.84 in)

Lighthouse Lens Orders

Beginning in 1823, Fresnel lenses were used in lighthouses to collimate light while significantly reducing the thickness and weight of a traditional convex lens. They were organized by size and focal length into six orders of power.

Beacon focal length (f) = 37.5 cm equivalent to 3 ½ order

Fresnel lens diameter 71.12 cm (28")

Equivalent convex lens with pilothouse viewport superimposed for comparison

90°

Collimated Light

Angle to clear dinghy

3°

$7.5° = \Theta_2$

Platform deck height

Beam Divergence:

Source size (y_1) of 5 cm assumed

$\Theta_2 = \arctan (y_1/f)$

$\Theta_2 = \arctan (5\ cm/37.5\ cm)$

$\Theta_2 = 7.5°$

Retraction cables and springs situated port and starboard between pressure hull stiffening ring bays

Scale: 5 cm = 1 m

0   1 m

ation mechanism might be. There were many ongoing experiments with incandescent light bulbs at the time; however, arc lamps were over 200 times brighter and more reliable. Perhaps, given Captain Nemo's account of using mercury in his propulsion chemistry, he has developed a mercury arc lamp, though early versions of these shared similar challenges of the carbon arc. A more sophisticated solution, especially suited for a sealed underwater housing, would be the mercury vapor lamp. This efficient, long-lasting, and bright lamp establishes an arc through a sealed container of vaporized mercury. It produces a blue-green light that is best suited for penetration in water. An early rudimentary mercury vapor lamp was developed in London by John Way in 1860, though a practical commercialized lamp would not be available until the turn of the century.[35] Until displaced by LEDs, such lights were common in modern deep ocean submersibles.

The electric beacon is contained within an 80 cm diameter spherical pressure vessel, which is cast with a pedestal base. Suspension cables, connected to springs located between frame bays, offset the weight of the beacon to allow for easy retraction and extension. Inside, a spherical mirror is set one focal length behind, and a Fresnel lens one focal length in front, of the light source. By the middle of the 19th century, such lenses were in wide use in lighthouse construction. Typically they were much larger and made up of many glass elements carefully configured in a supporting framework. The lens on the *Nautilus*, for practical reasons, is a single-piece construction, and thus its fabrication

would demand significant sophistication for the period. Although Captain Nemo does not disclose the source of his lens and glass viewports, almost certainly they would have been manufactured by Chance Brothers and Company of Smethwick, England. The company was originally established in 1824 making blown glass for windows. By the middle of the century they were the leading glass manufacturer in England and tremendous innovators who capitalized on the expertise of Georges Bontemps, a pioneering French glassmaker who was forced to flee France during the revolution of 1848. They introduced a novel process for rolled plate glass production that allowed the construction of London's Crystal Palace in 1851 using sheets of glass measuring 10"x49", the largest able to be made in the world at the time. They also became a major lighthouse engineering company producing optical components, and led the transition to electric arc lanterns. At Dungeness, a six-inch radius model ran continuously for three years beginning in 1862, but with less than satisfactory results. At the Paris Exposition in 1867 they demonstrated a third order (20-inch radius) apparatus with electric light that provided Verne a model to describe for the *Nautilus*.[36] Chance Brothers probably represented the only company in the world in 1860 with the manufacturing capability and creative capacity to have been able to fabricate the lenses of the electric beacon, the 21 cm thick biconvex viewports of the pilothouse, and the enormous salon windows of sufficient thickness and proper shape necessary to resist pressure at even modest depths.

THE PILOTHOUSE

"'The helmsman is stationed in a glass-windowed pilothouse that protrudes above the hull; biconvex lenses are set in the walls. ...I use glass windows measuring no less than 21 centimeters at their center...'" p. 88

"It was a cabin about six feet square, closely resembling those occupied by the helmsmen of steamboats plying the Mississippi and Hudson rivers. In the center stood an upright wheel geared to rudder cables running to the *Nautilus's* stern. Four deadlights, windows of biconvex glass, were set one in each wall, enabling the man at the helm to see in every direction." pp. 228–230

"Electric wires linked the pilothouse with the engine room, and...the captain could signal simultaneously the direction and the speed he desired. He pressed a metal button and at once the propeller slowed down considerably." p. 230

"Captain Nemo never took his eyes off the two concentric circles of the compass hanging in the cabin." p. 230

Although described as "six feet square," the design loosely interprets this as a floor area estimate for a 1.5 meter diameter cylindrical structure with a spherical cap optimized to resist pressure. On the outside of this pressure boundary is depicted a five-sided armored structure that conforms to both the description and the woodcut illustrations of the wheelhouse appearance. The center of each side is tangent to the surface of the pressure hull and coincident with the center of each viewport. The angles of the viewports provided by the sides of a pentagon gives a good field of view while avoiding the light from directly astern, and the forward vertex affords some additional collision protection. The geometry described for the viewports has the effect of generating a small magnification, and the restricted dimensions of the pilothouse result in a convergence of the viewport focal points in a small circle centered on the helmsman. When the pilothouse is extended, a two-step platform places the helmsman's eye at window center.

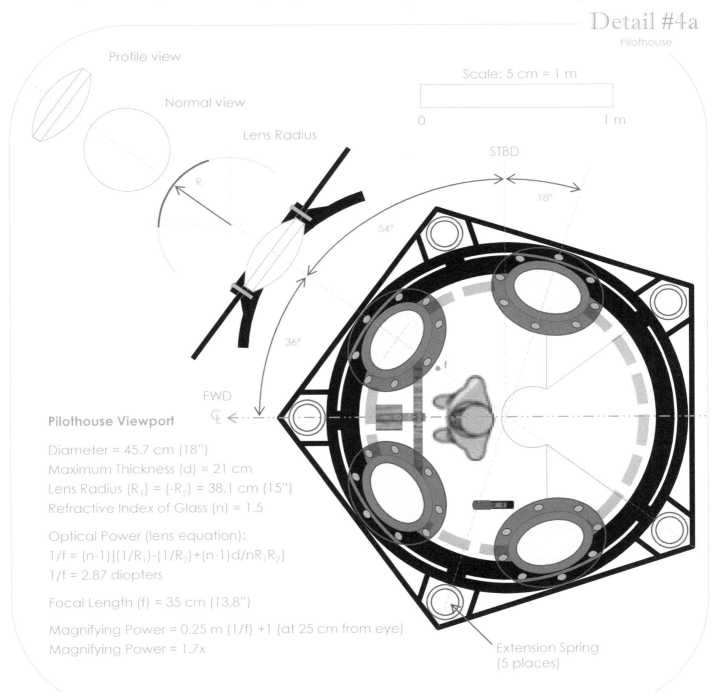

Detail #4a
Pilothouse

Profile view

Normal view

Lens Radius

R_1

Scale: 5 cm = 1 m

0   1 m

STBD

18°

54°

36°

FWD

Pilothouse Viewport

Diameter = 45.7 cm (18")
Maximum Thickness (d) = 21 cm
Lens Radius (R_1) = ($-R_2$) = 38.1 cm (15")
Refractive Index of Glass (n) = 1.5

Optical Power (lens equation):
$1/f = (n-1)[(1/R_1)-(1/R_2)+(n-1)d/nR_1R_2]$
$1/f$ = 2.87 diopters

Focal Length (f) = 35 cm (13.8")

Magnifying Power = 0.25 m (1/f) +1 (at 25 cm from eye)
Magnifying Power = 1.7x

Extension Spring
(5 places)

It must be acknowledged that a consequence of this design is that the pilothouse viewports are likely to be awash while on the surface at any significant speed, and the height-of-eye afforded the helmsman provides, at best, only 2.5 nm of visibility to the horizon. Of course, the solution to this problem is the periscope, which was invented in 1854 by Hippolyte Marié-Davy, a French chemist who later became the Deputy Director of the Paris Observatory[37]. In that same year he also invented an electromagnetic motor and a mercury bisulfate battery (that McClintock originally planned to install in *H.L. Hunley*), and it is possible that his proposal for a submarine with an electrically driven propeller may have inspired the *Nautilus's* locomotion.[38] It is curious then, why Captain Nemo did not also incorporate a periscope, which quickly found its way into the design of the submarines *Peral* and *Gymnote* in 1888, and Simon Lake's *Protector* of 1902.

During the infrequent occasions when the pilothouse is retracted, the helmsman must operate either from a crouched position or standing one step down in the cutout provided, which maintains his height-of-eye near the window center. In this condition, a small portion of the forward viewports

remains exposed above the curve of the hull, which affords the helmsman a restricted view ahead, but one that is adequate for ramming. The upper portion of the wheelhouse is pushed into the lower doubled-walled pressure boundary against the force of five extension springs housed in the vertices of the outer pentagon shell. The springs offset the considerable weight of the upper pilothouse structure, and a simple latch mechanism maintains the retracted position. The upper wall contains a cutout that provides clearance over the connection between the double lower walls needed for the access hatch to the upper passage. In the raised position, five extension braces must be manually inserted between flanges cast into the upper pilothouse structure, and the lower pressure wall, in order to resist compression of the pilothouse by sea pressure. This bracing between the viewports evokes the structure shown in figure 15. The helm is conventional, and the rudder control cables exit the port side of the pilothouse from below the helmsman's platform into the equipment space above the library, and then run aft on the port side, below and therefore outboard of the service air header. In the aft, port end of the engine room, the cables are wound around a drum to provide me-

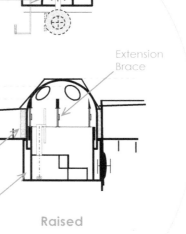

Pilothouse Cupola
(looking forward)

Cutout over
access hatch

Helmsman's Visibility

Extension
Brace

Extension
Springs

Lowered

Retraction
Cavity
(equalized to sea pressure)

Raised

Scale: 1 cm = 1 m

0   1   2   3   4

Detail #4b

chanical advantage to the rack and pinion gear that moves the rudder yoke. A weighted loop just forward of the drum maintains tension on the control cable and accommodates slack in the shorter cable leg when the rudder is swung port or starboard from center line. A lever on the port side of the helmsman station controls the position of the forward planes through a mechanical linkage located in the equipment space above the library. This affords the helmsman precise and timely depth con-

Figure 15: The pilothouse

trol. Two valves on the port side supply air or vent the piston that operates the shutters covering the salon viewports. Propulsion orders and desired depth or pitch angle are transmitted to the engine room watch-stander via an electric annunciator system. Repeater stations in the salon and his stateroom also allow Captain Nemo to transmit some basic orders (surface, dive, open/close shutters) to the helmsman using a pre-arranged code. A prominently mounted compass is specifically noted by Professor Aronnax; however, instrumentation to indicate speed and depth must also be available in the pilothouse.

THE DINGHY

"Near the middle of the platform the dinghy was half buried in the hull, forming a slight bulge." p. 91

"'The dinghy is attached to the topside of the *Nautilus's* hull. It's set in a cavity made expressly to receive it. It's decked over, completely watertight, held in place with strong bolts. This ladder takes me up to a hatch in the hull of the *Nautilus* that corresponds to a similar hatch in the side of the dinghy. Through that double opening I can enter the dinghy. The crew close up the hatch in the *Nautilus*, I close up the one in the longboat, simply by screwing it into place. I undo the bolts holding the dinghy to the *Nautilus*, and the dinghy shoots to the surface. Then I open the paneling of the deck, kept closed until now, step my mast and hoist my sail—or I set my oars—and I'm off!'" p. 81

"'An electric cable connects us. I telegraph my orders to the ship.'" p. 80

"...the dinghy, its deck panels opened, was wrenched from its socket and launched into the sea. Only two men were needed for that task." p. 143

"Oars in position, five of the *Nautilus's* crew were already aboard the dinghy, which was now moored alongside... Captain Nemo, Conseil, Ned, and I found seats in the stern of the dinghy. The coxswain took the tiller, his four crewmen leaned into their oars..." pp. 200–201

"The dinghy was pushed off, and driven along by its six oarsmen..." p. 225

"Half overturned, it [the dinghy] shipped a few tons of water that we had to bail out." p. 226

"Hoisted back on board, the dinghy was set down in its socket..." p. 238

There are several challenges associated with deriving an appropriate design for the dinghy. It is described as half buried in the hull and forming only a slight bulge, and yet can easily be extracted and launched by two crewmembers. During their brief sojourn on land, the dinghy is made out to be a small rowboat capable of being handled by two unskilled oarsmen (Conseil and Professor Aronnax), yet during the fight

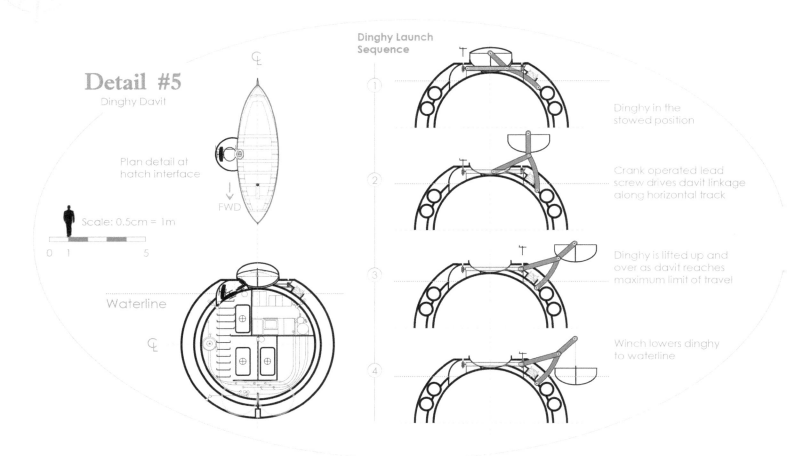

Detail #5
Dinghy Davit

Plan detail at
hatch interface

Scale: 0.5cm = 1m

0 1   5

Waterline

Dinghy Launch
Sequence

① Dinghy in the
stowed position

② Crank operated lead
screw drives davit linkage
along horizontal track

③ Dinghy is lifted up and
over as davit reaches
maximum limit of travel

④ Winch lowers dinghy
to waterline

with the dugong it can easily accommodate ten personnel with room for Captain Nemo, who declines to join. Since it is capable of being launched from underwater, the dinghy must also be a pressure vessel capable of resisting the same depths as the *Nautilus*, and yet the upper decking enclosing the dinghy is light enough to be easily removed by Captain Nemo alone when using it for excursions on the surface. These incongruities and more make closing on a single design for the dinghy quite challenging. A model of the French submarine *Plongeur* (figure 16) was displayed at the 1867 Exposition Universelle, where it was studied by Jules Verne, who used it as inspiration. This vessel had a small lifeboat mounted topside that measured 8 m x 1.7 m to allow for escape of the twelve-man crew.[40] It seems reasonable to assume that Captain Nemo would have sized his dinghy to be able to serve as a lifeboat for his entire crew, some twenty-three persons. We have chosen to make the dinghy 8 m x 2.2 m, which represents a compromise between small size and the ability to accommodate all aboard the *Nautilus*. Consider that the HMS *Bounty*'s launch measured 7 m x 2 m, and though grossly overloaded, was able to carry nineteen men 3,618 nm over forty-seven days.[41] In the event that the dinghy would be used to evacuate the *Nautilus*, the crew

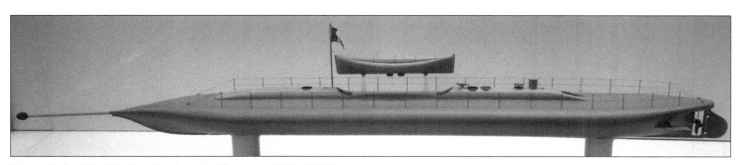

Figure 16: Model of the French submarine Plongeur *(1863-1872)*[39]

Figure 17: Depictions of the dinghy from early woodcut illustrations

could be expected to lay below the thwarts and also across them on top, for the short trip to the surface.

The dinghy, like the *Nautilus*, is constructed of steel. This was hardly unheard of in the mid 19th century, as the success of the Francis' Metallic Life-Boat Company had well established the practicality of a metal boat and its advantages over wood construction. Copper or iron could be stamped in a hydraulic press to form lightweight boat halves that incorporated longitudinal corrugations, somewhat akin to conventional strakes, for strength. Boats comparable in size to the *Nautilus's* dinghy came into widespread use on passenger steamers and among the U.S. Life Saving Stations along the Atlantic Coast. They featured sealed air chambers in the bow and stern that rendered them unsinkable even if swamped.[42] The dinghy's lines echo the stalwart form of a New Bedford whaleboat, however the gunwales have been raised amidships to provide a level interface for engaging the cover. This also improves freeboard, which is most acute during an emergency egress when the weight of the cover and a full complement of crew must be considered. As a necessary compromise between buoyancy and pressure resistance, the dinghy hull has been made 2 cm thick, with the benches serving as lateral stanchions to strengthen the dinghy walls against compression buckling. Another compromise is required for the dinghy's decking. Lightweight, flat, sectional

plates as described in the text are inadequate to resist the pressure at the *Nautilus's* full operational depth. Some have proposed inverting the dinghy, so that the rounded hull is exposed to pressure and the upper deck is protected against the *Nautilus's* hull, however this does not allow the dinghy to be used as an underwater escape pod, for once detached, the exposed decking will immediately be subjected to pressure. The alternative we have chosen is to interpret the dinghy deck panels as forming a hemispherical cap that provides a modest improvement to resist pressure. The seal around the gunwale necessitates that the tiller be removable; stowed in the dinghy and installed once the deck is removed. Launch of the dinghy on the surface is shown in detail #5. Recovery of the boat is accomplished in the reverse manner with the tension of the davit ensuring a snug fit against the large rubber seal surrounding the starboard access hatch. During an underwater launch, the dinghy is released by unscrewing the pins connecting the bow and stern to the davit arms. After launch, the transfer trunk floods, however, it is equipped with a drain for dewatering on the surface during dinghy recovery.

Figure 18: Francis lifeboat patent model

Submarine Development

Dr. Antoine Prosper Payerne, a French doctor experimenting with air replenishment in enclosed spaces, developed a diving bell in 1844, and then a diving boat called Belledonne in 1846. Its thirty-five-foot length contained an air reservoir, a hand-cranked propeller, and a small air lock to permit divers to egress. It pioneered the use of quicklime to remove carbon dioxide from the atmosphere.

Lambert Alexandre, a salvage diver from France and one-time associate of Dr. Payerne, relocated to New York and built the Submarine Explorer, which was a two-chambered diving bell able to be propelled by a hand-crank and steered by vertical and horizontal rudders.

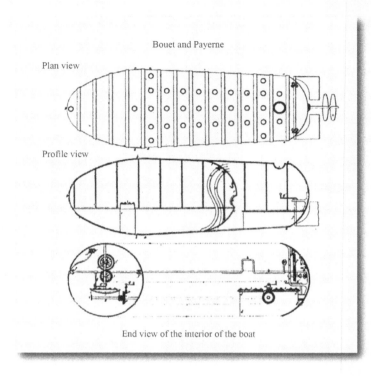

Bouet and Payerne

Plan view

Profile view

End view of the interior of the boat

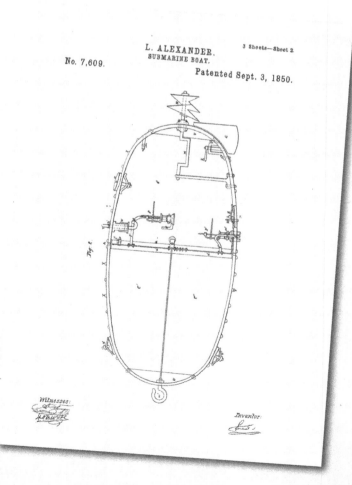

No. 7,609.

L. ALEXANDER.
SUBMARINE BOAT.

3 Sheets—Sheet 2.

Patented Sept. 3, 1850.

Witnesses:

Inventor:

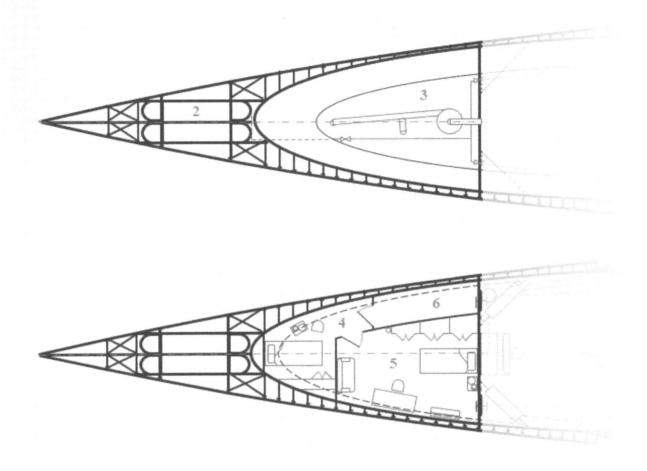

First Compartment

INTERIOR LAYOUT – FIRST COMPARTMENT

"So then, I already knew the whole forward part of this submarine boat. I reviewed its subdivisions in my mind going from amidships to the ram on its prow: the dining hall, five meters long, separated from the library by a watertight bulkhead; the library, also five meters long; the grand salon, ten meters long, separated from the captain's cabin by a second watertight bulkhead; the captain's room, five meters; mine, two-and-a-half meters; and lastly, air tanks, extending about seven-and-a-half meters to the stem post. All together, a length of thirty-five meters." p. 80

"I followed Captain Nemo. Through one of the doorways that pierced the canted corners of the salon he led me again into the corridors, toward the bow. There I found not just a cabin but an elegant room with a bed, a washstand, and other furniture." p. 76

"'Your room adjoins mine,' he said as he opened another door, 'and mine opens into the salon we just left.' I went into his room. It had a severe, almost monastic air. A small iron bedstead, a worktable, a washstand, and very subdued lighting. No luxuries. Just the barest necessities. He pointed to a bench." p. 76

"…I came to the door, set into one of the canted corners, that led into the captain's cabin." p. 255

"I went back to my cabin… I put my ear to the captain's door… I left my room and went back to the salon… I opened the door to the library… I went over…near the door that led to the central companionway." p. 256

"I went back to my cabin, where I could hear movements inside Captain Nemo's quarters. I knocked on his door." p. 358

"He [Captain Nemo] was out there in the salon, which I would have to walk through in order to escape." p. 383

"I moved slowly through the *Nautilus's* dark corridors… I reached the corner door of the salon…" p. 383

The interior divisions along the longitudinal axis from the bow to amidships are well detailed. The key design decision lies in locating the specific deck height, which has been selected to optimize the floor space as well as conform to the descriptions provided. We have chosen to make the air reservoirs in the bow cylindrical structures separate from the pressure hull. This would be the most practical construction method in this narrow space with tight radius curves. It is also considerably safer to locate volumes of highly compressed air outside the pressure hull, and in doing so they contribute to the total submerged displacement volume. The high-pressure air piping enters the pressure hull just above Captain Nemo's cabin, and an isolation valve is easily accessible in the overhead. The pipe then splits into a port and starboard header, penetrating the watertight bulkhead over each watertight door to the salon. An isolation valve in the overhead behind the canted corners of the salon provides watertight integrity.

Given societal norms of the period and Captain Nemo's royal pedigree, it seems likely that Aronnax's small cabin was previously used by whichever crew member was assigned as Captain Nemo's valet. A small decorative panel in this room disguises the sharply concave end of the spheroid hull form. The short corridor in the bow would have allowed the valet access to the room without disturbing Captain Nemo, and follows the design principle that every watertight compartment should have two exits. Captain Nemo's cabin is adorned only with the ship's instruments and "On the far wall [opposite the entrance

Figure 19: Nemo's cabin

from the salon] beneath the [seven] portraits of his heroes...the portrait of a still young woman with two little children" (p. 379). The forward variable ballast tank is located in the lower part of this compartment, providing the maximum lever arm for adjusting trim. It is vented to the ship's atmosphere through a pipe in Captain Nemo's room that exhausts in the over-head space. This space also contains ventilation ducts equipped with electric heating elements and a fan to circulate air from the salon into the cabins since this compartment is not supplied with air from the ship's distribution trunk. A bulkhead isolation damper is provided in the overhead to isolate the penetration to the salon.

"'I'm sure you recognize some of these like the thermometer, which gives me the temperature inside the boat; the barometer, which tells me the weight of the outside air and so helps me anticipate changes in the weather; the humidistat [hygrometer], which indicates the degree of dryness in the atmosphere; the storm glass, whose contents, if they decompose, foretell the approach of tempests; the compass, which directs my course; the sextant, with which I can shoot the altitude of the sun and so determine my latitude; chronometers, with which I reckon my longitude; and telescopes for day or night, with which I can survey the horizon when I go to the surface.'" p. 77

"'This dial with the moving needle—isn't this a pressure gauge?' 'Actually, yes. But in showing me the water pressure on our hull, it also shows me how deep down we are.' 'And these seem to be a new kind of sounding line.' 'They're thermometric sounding lines. They report temperatures in the different strata of the sea.'" p. 77

"'...this dial hanging before our eyes indicates the speed of the *Nautilus*. An electric cable connects it to a patent log, and this needle shows our actual progress...'" p. 79

The *Nautilus* is equipped with instruments that would be considered standard fare for shipboard navigation, namely a sextant for determining latitude and a chronometer to assist the determination of longitude. But precisely fixing the *Nautilus's* position on the bottom for diver operations would be a significant challenge with such tools, and remains difficult even with modern technology. To keep track of his position between celestial fixes, Captain Nemo employs dead reckoning; a calculation of position based on the speed, direction, and duration of travel from a known fix. This requires a patent log to measure the speed of the *Nautilus* through the water, and a magnetic compass to determine heading. Since heaving the log overboard, as was the practice in days of sail, is not practical, it is almost certainly permanently affixed to a point outside the hull and transmits an electric signal to an indicator inside. The side of the keel, well forward of the rudder, is a reasonable mounting location below the surfaced waterline that avoids damage when bottomed, is removed from the turbulence of the propeller, and is unlikely to foul the drag nets that are towed astern. As for the compass, little mention is made of the details of that installation, but getting one to function correctly inside an iron sub-marine is not a trivial matter. Even wooden sailing ships possessed sufficient sources of influence to induce deviation in compasses carried on board, and the introduction of iron ships exacerbated the problem tremendously. The solution required mounting the compass in a fixed location and then arranging a system of iron bars and balls around the compass in such a way to offset the magnetic deviation caused by the ship. This assembly is called a binnacle. In 1854, John Gray patented a new binnacle that incorporated correcting magnets able to be moved by screws and racks and pinions, eliminating the awkward permanent installation of iron masses on the deck around the compass. It also incorporated a vertical magnet, known as a Flinder's bar, that corrected for deviations caused by the ship heeling.[43] As with the earlier solutions, establishing the correct arrangement of compensating iron or magnets required swinging a ship to various headings, precisely determined by reference to landmarks on shore, and then noting the compass deviation from the known heading. This practice was well established by the mid-19th century, thus it is curious that there is little mention of a binnacle in the *Nautilus* beyond the oblique reference to, "two concentric circles of the compass hanging in the [pilothouse]"

(p. 230). The obvious interpretation is that this describes the two gimbals within which the compass is mounted to remain independent of pitch and roll motion. The lack of detail regarding mechanisms to compensate for deviation may reflect Professor Arronax's ignorance as an observer, or that possibly such components have been affixed to the pilothouse wall and within the steering pedestal or helmsman's platform in a manner that obscures their connection with the compass. Since it seems impractical to swing and correct a compass installed as part of the instruments in the salon, engine room, and Captain Nemo's cabin, it is probable that these are electro-mechanical repeaters of heading indication provided by the binnacle in the pilothouse.

For a submarine, instruments to measure water temperature and pressure and to record stratifications of temperature and salinity with depth, are all important and require some connection with the sea outside the hull. A sensing line could be a dedicated hull penetration or tapped off an existing suction, discharge or cavity drain line. The compensated cavity that the upper portion of the pilothouse retracts into provides a convenient sample point and correlates with the hypothesis that the *Nautilus's* depth is referenced to a level near that of the platform. This suggests that these instruments in the salon, engine room, and Captain Nemo's cabin, may be repeaters as well. The measurement of sea pressure provides the means for indicating ship's depth, and an inclinometer, though not specifically mentioned, is the final instrument needed for ship control. To monitor the condition of his power supply, conventional voltmeters and ammeters are provided. When the *Nautilus* is surfaced, local meteorological conditions can be ascertained by using a thermometer, barometer, and hygrometer. The storm glass that Captain Nemo mentions became popular in the 1860s after being promoted by Admiral Robert Fitzroy, former captain of HMS *Beagle* and founder of the Meteorological Office.[44] It was claimed to be able to forecast changes in weather, even drawing distinctions between various types of expected precipitation, based on the formation of crystals suspended in a proprietary liquid sealed inside the glass. However, modern science has demonstrated that temperature alone is responsible for the crystal formation, and the utility of the instrument in weather forecasting is nil.

Nautilus's Instruments

19th century maritime instruments representative of those on the *Nautilus*

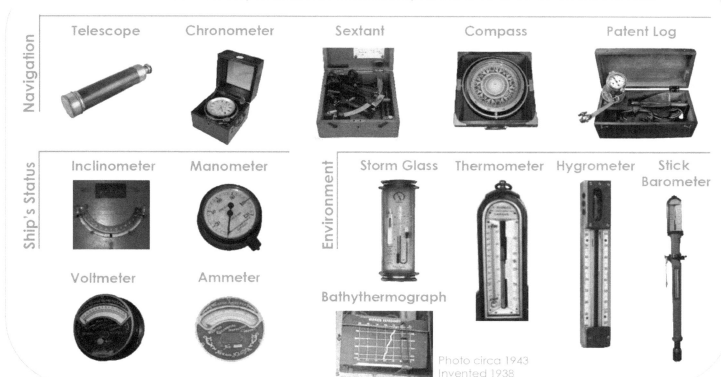

Navigation
Telescope   Chronometer   Sextant   Compass   Patent Log

Ship's Status
Inclinometer   Manometer
Voltmeter   Ammeter

Environment
Storm Glass   Thermometer   Hygrometer   Stick Barometer

Bathythermograph

Photo circa 1943
Invented 1938

Captain Nemo's
Portrait Etchings[45]

Thaddeus Kosciusko – a skilled Polish engineer, in 1776 he offered his services to the American revolutionary cause, masterminding a key British defeat at Saratoga and building the fortifications at West Point. After the war, he returned to Poland and led a valiant but ultimately unsuccessful uprising against the nation's partition by Russia and other foreign powers. After several years of imprisonment in Russia, he returned to the United States, where he was welcomed as a hero. With Poland still under foreign control throughout the rest of his life, he never returned to his native land, and died in exile in Switzerland in 1817.

Markos Botzaris – among the most revered national heroes of Greece, General Botzaris was a leader in the Greek War of Independence against the Ottoman Empire. He was courageous in the defense of Missolonghi during the first siege of the city from 1822 to 1823. Killed while leading the attack on Karpensi in August 1823, he was buried with full honors. His brother, son and daughter went on to long and distinguished service to the Greek state.

Daniel O'Connell – known as "The Liberator," he was a lawyer who campaigned for Catholic emancipation—including the right for Catholics to sit in the Westminster Parliament, denied for over 100 years—and repeal of the Act of Union which combined Great Britain and Ireland. He rejected rebellion and consistently worked through political reform and public activism. He was opposed to slavery, and his philosophy and approach served as inspiration to Frederick Douglass, Mahatma Gandhi, and Martin Luther King, among others.

George Washington – one of the Founding Fathers of the United States of America, he served as Commander-in-Chief during the War of Independence against Great Britain, as chairman of the 1787 Constitutional Convention, and as the first President, establishing a strong, well-financed national government. His resignation as Commander-in-Chief and self-imposed two-term limit as President set an example, previously unseen in history, of the subordination of military to civilian authority and the peaceful transition of power.

Daniele Manin – an Italian patriot and statesman who was imprisoned resisting the occupation of Venetia by Austria. Following the rebellion of 1849, he was freed and made president of the Venetian republic and then resigned his powers in pursuit of Italian unification. With the return of the Austrians, he was again chosen as President and led a heroic defense of Venice against an Austrian siege, until cholera and bombardment finally forced surrender. Manin was excepted from amnesty and banished. For the remainder of his life he lived in Paris, where he strove to enlist French sympathy for the Italian cause.

Abraham Lincoln – a self-taught lawyer and an American legislator who served as the President of the United States from March 1861 until his assassination in April 1865. He led the United States through its Civil War—its bloodiest war and perhaps its greatest moral, constitutional, and political crisis. In doing so, he preserved the Union, abolished slavery, strengthened the federal government, and modernized the economy.

John Brown – a radical abolitionist who believed in the violent overthrow of the slavery system and led attacks on pro-slavery residents in Kansas. In 1859, Brown and 21 of his followers attacked and occupied the federal arsenal in Harpers Ferry. Their goal was to capture supplies and use them to arm a slave rebellion. Brown was captured during the raid and later hanged, but not before becoming an anti-slavery icon.

This is the actual image alluded to in the text
Death of John Brown by Victor Hugo, 1860.

Submarine Development

Following the work of Alexandre, diving bell design proliferated. One of the few successfully employed, the "Nautilus Diving Bell," was developed by Edgar Foreman and Henry Sears in New York. It incorporated floodable ballast chambers which were controlled by the operator and used for salvage from 1856 to 1860. The Nautilus bell inspired Van Buren Ryerson to design a more sophisticated two-chambered diving bell called the Submarine Explorer, which dispensed with the surface air hose by incorporating a compressed air chamber between the inner and outer shells. Julius Kroehl employed the bell to complete a harbor clearing contract in New York, and it served as the basis for his design of the Sub Marine Explorer constructed in 1865 for a failed speculative venture to harvest pearls in Panama.

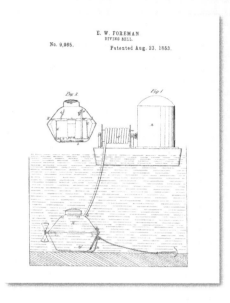

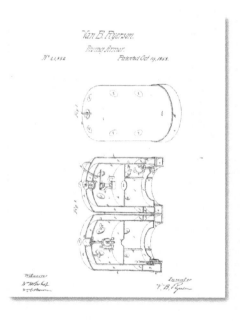

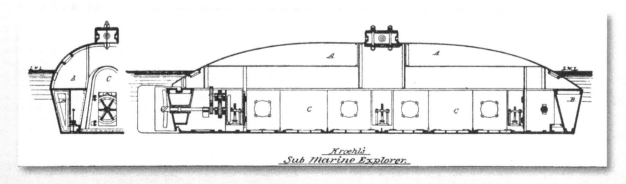

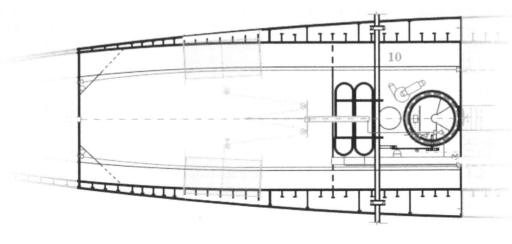

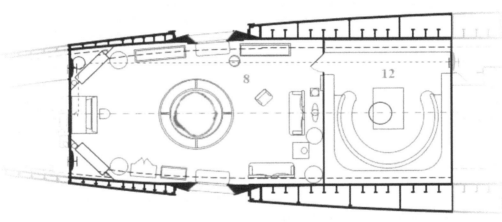

Second Compartment

INTERIOR LAYOUT – SECOND COMPARTMENT

"At the rear of the dining room a double door opened and I entered another room of about the same size. It was a library. Tall pieces of furniture, made of black rosewood inlaid with copper, contained in their deep shelves a vast number of books uniformly bound. These bookcases followed the contours of the room, leading at the lower end to long couches upholstered in maroon leather and curved to provide maximum comfort. There were light, movable reading stands on which one could rest a book and which could be pulled over or pushed away as one required. In the center of the room stood an immense table, covered with pamphlets and newspapers way out of date. Electric light originating in four frosted globes half-set in the ceiling, flooded the whole harmonious ensemble." p. 71

"Captain Nemo now opened a door facing the one by which we had entered the library, and I passed into an immense salon splendidly lighted. It was a large quadrilateral with corners canted, ten meters long, six wide, and five high. A luminous ceiling, decorated with light arabesques, shed a gentle light, clear as day, over all the marvels assembled in this—museum....on pedestals in the corners of this magnificent museum stood some admirable statues in marble or bronze modeled on some of the loveliest works of antiquity." p. 73

"Some thirty pictures by the masters, uniformly framed and separated by glittering panoplies of arms, decorated the walls, which were hung with tapestries of severe, classic design." p. 73

"I pointed to sheet music...scattered over a large organ standing against one wall of the salon." p. 74

"In the middle of the salon a jet of water, lighted by electricity, tumbled back into a large bowl made from a single giant clam. Its rim was delicately scalloped and measured about six meters in circumference." p. 74

"Around this fountain, in elegant glass cases framed in copper, I found the most precious specimens of the sea..." p. 74

"...a cabinet near the port panel...turned out to be a kind of safe containing a great number of ingots." p. 238

A consequence of the spindle-shaped outer hull and spheroid-shaped inner hull is an adequate enclosed volume to encompass the dimensions given for the salon. There is extensive reinforcement between the hulls in this area both because of the force transmitted by the ram, and because the hull transitions from a spheroid to cylindrical cross section, creating a stress concentration that is not reinforced with an interior watertight bulkhead as is the case aft. This being the point where the inner and outer hulls are closest together, it is the natural location for the viewports. They are mounted on the horizontal mid-plane, sufficiently forward of the frame marking the hull transition so as to not further complicate welding or concentrate stress at this critical juncture. Locations farther forward do not provide sufficient clearance for the shutter door and would be inconsistent with the illustration. The operating piston and associated tackle for the shutters are located in the space between the hulls above this compartment. The salon furnishings shown in the plan are consistent with the extensive description and include, "some instruments entirely unfamiliar to [Aronnax]" (p. 76). The canted corners at the forward end of the room mask the watertight doors, which would be incongruous with the décor, and they allow for a transition of one step down from the cabins forward to the salon deck height. In the aft starboard corner of the salon is the door to the library.

The library makes up the aft end of this compartment and the professor is surprised to learn that it contains 12,000 books. At the outset of the 19th century, libraries were small; Harvard College, possessing the largest collection in the United States, had 12,000 volumes in 1790. Following its destruction in the 1812 war, the Library of Congress was founded with the 6,487 books contained in Thomas Jefferson's library, considered one of the finest personal collections of its time.[46] By mid-century the collection would number 55,000 books, and in 1854, Boston Public Library and the Astor Library, forerunner to the New York Public Library, opened with 16,000 and 80,000 books, respectively.[47] The oldest and largest libraries of Europe at this time included the University Oxford's Bodleian Library, which had 220,000 books and 21,000 manuscripts in 1849, and the Bibliotheque Nationale, or National Library of France, which, through confiscations of church

Figure 20: The library

and rich nobles' libraries, had amassed the largest repository of books in the world with some 650,000 volumes.[48] This provides perspective on Captain Nemo's private library which, for its time, can be regarded as quite impressive and of course, all the more amazing in that it is housed aboard a submarine.

The woodcut illustration depicts a library of about 1,200 books, and a quick calculation of the available shelf space in the deck plan illustrates the challenge of accommodating an inventory of 12,000. The shelves on the forward and aft walls are each 35 cm deep, while the ones to port and starboard vary up to 50 cm deep on account of the hull curvature. The hull would need to be well insulated here, typically with several inches of cork, to prevent condensation damage to the books. The total frontal shelf area available in the library is 59.4 m², which assumes books behind the seat cushions, under the benches, and over the door to the salon and the hatch to the passageway. Although many variations are possible, twelve shelves, each 26.25 cm in height, fit nicely within the 3.15 m ceiling height provided. To accommodate 12,000 volumes, each is assumed to be 26 cm high, which results in an average width of 1.9 cm. This is a reasonable, if somewhat slim, result, and

the precision required, along with the observation that they are uniformly bound, suggests that Captain Nemo almost certainly had them specially printed for this space. One option, common in libraries to increase storage density, would be to incorporate a second layer of sliding bookcases in front of the ones mounted to the bulkheads.

The height of the library ceiling is never specified, but implied to be noticeably lower than the salon. This provides space above for the pilothouse to retract into. Mechanical and electrical penetrations to the pilothouse enter at floor level to avoid interfering with retraction. Forward of the pilothouse is a crawlspace, accessible via a bolted plate in the library ceiling, that accommodates the internal ship's service air flasks. These reservoirs provide compressed air to pressurize potable water delivery, blow the sanitary waste tank overboard when the sub is at a shallow depth, fill diving apparatus, open the salon shutter doors, operate the dive chamber egress ramp winch, and even supply the pipe organ.

The high-pressure air headers pass through this space from the overhead of the salon, where they are concealed in the crown molding, on their way to the main ballast tanks. Isolation valves, normally kept open, are provided at the bulkhead penetration. Ventilation ductwork routed through this space supplies the library and salon. A separate fan recirculates the air in the library through a charcoal filter, allowing the space to be used "as a smoking room," as Captain Nemo proudly points out. The efficacy of plain and activated charcoal at removing odors from air had been generally recognized since the early 19th century. But the development of specific filters for the removal of noxious contaminants was the work of Scottish scientist John Stenhouse, who developed protective breathing masks in the mid 1850s.[49]

Beneath the deck of the salon and library is the auxiliary battery well, accessed through a bolted access plate in the library floor. The two access plates in the library are vertically aligned with an overhead hull plug to permit in-port removal of individual battery

cells. Since details are lacking in the text, these 198 cells (each measuring 0.4 m x 0.5 m x 1 m) are modeled on conventional lead-acid batteries used in fleet boats of the WWII era. Whatever their composition, they are presumed to be a backup to Captain Nemo's mysterious primary power source, and their location in this compartment is necessary to balance the large and relatively empty rooms forward with the weight of the machinery-dense compartments farther aft. In the event that the battery chemistry has the potential to generate hazardous gas, which is frequently the case, a small ventilation blower is located just forward of the cells. It is designed to prevent accumulation that would lead to dangerous concentrations by drawing air from the battery well via two small ducts that rise behind the canted corners of the salon.

Figure 21: Depictions of the salon in early woodcut illustrations

SALON ARTWORK

The decoration of the salon reflects an 1859 visit by Verne to Inzievar House in Oakley, Scotland[50], and the style of furnishings shown here are typical for the period. Marble statues of Poseidon (god of the sea) and Athena (goddess of wisdom and military victory) and a bronze casting of Hercules (divine hero) seem appropriate selections to represent the sculpture noted but not specified by Professor Aronnax. Armaments and tapestries depicted are 18th–19th century Indian styling reflecting Captain Nemo's heritage as Prince Dakkar. Various masterpieces of Chinese and Greek pottery, and European armor and silver-smithing, are included to conform with the woodcut illustrations. While the exact paintings selected by Captain Nemo are not specified and have been presumably lost to mankind, representations of the artists and subjects noted by Professor Aronnax provide a feel for the décor of the salon. Canvas sizes are original unless otherwise noted. One can imagine the significant challenge of regulating the *Nautilus's* temperature and humidity sufficiently to avoid rapid deterioration of these artworks.

a) *Jupiter and Io*, Antonio Allegri da Correggio (c. 1530)

b) *Landscape with a Pond*, Charles Daubigny (1861)

c) *The Hunter's Gift*, Gabriël Metsu (1660)

d) *The Battle of Vigo Bay*, Ludolf Backhuysen (c. 1702)

e) *The Artist's Family*, Hans Holbein (1528)

f) *Country Kermess* paintings, David Teniers (1650)

g) *Shipwreck*, Claude Joseph Vernet (1772)

h) *The Hunt*, Alexandre Decamps (1847)

i) *Napoleon's Stallion Tamerland*, Théodore Géricault (c. 1810)

j) *Flemish Kermess*, David Teniers (1652)

k) *Adoration of the Magi*, Paolo Veronese (c. 1570)

l) *Combat of the Giaour and the Pasha*, Eugène Delacroix (1827)

m) *Assumption of the Virgin*, Bartolemé Murillo (1690)

n) *The Virgin and Child with St. Anne*, Leonardo daVinci (c. 1508) (depicted at 80% size)

o) *Madonna of Belvedere*, Raphael (1506)

p) *Flora*, Titian (c. 1515)

q) *The Village Fete*, Peter Paul Rubens (1638)

r) *Beach at Trouville*, Constant Troyon (c. 1840)

s) *Martyrdom of Saint Bartholomew*, Jusepe Ribera (1634)

t) *Joan of Arc at the Coronation of Charles VII*, Jean Ingres (1854) (depicted at 40% size)

u) *Children with a Rabbit*, Pierre Paul Prudhon (1814)

v) *Old Woman with a Candle*, Gerard Dow (c. 1630)

w) *Horses in a Field*, Paulus Potter (1649)

x) *St. Anthony Abbott*, Diego Velázquez (1638)

y) *Memory of a Civil War*, Jean-Louis Ernest Meissonier (1849)

Detail #6
Salon Artwork

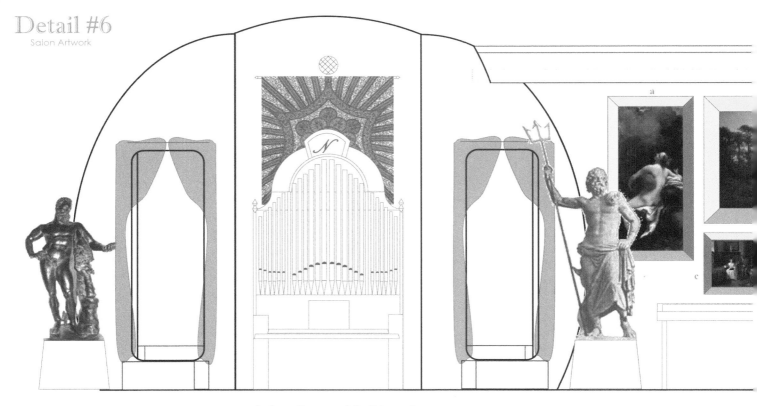

Salon, Forward Bulkhead

Salon, Aft Bulkhead

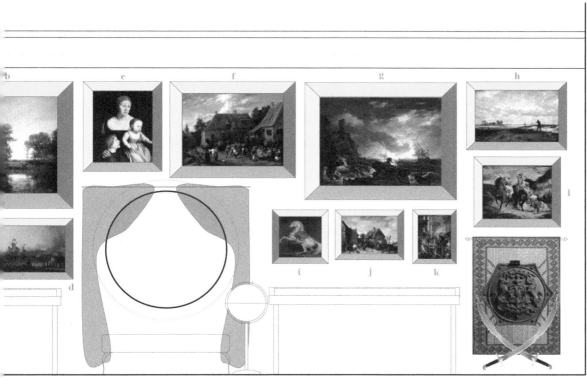

Salon, Starboard Side

Scale: 2.5 cm = 1 m

0   1   2

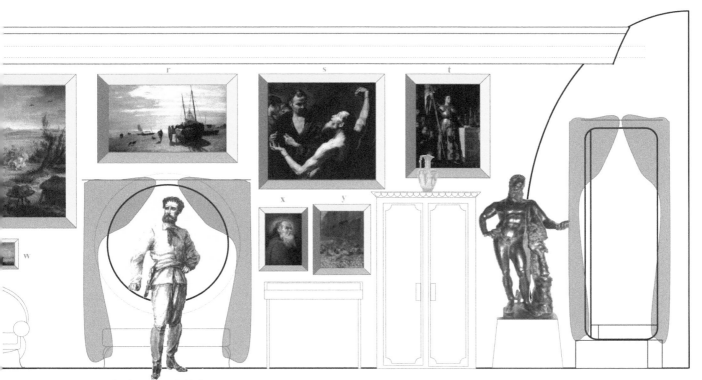

Salon, Port Side

Submarine Development

Lodner Phillips was a Chicago shoemaker who experimented with building two submarines before constructing his Marine Cigar in 1851. It was 40 ft long, had a hand-cranked two-blade propeller, and contrived to refresh the air inside by percolating it through the ballast tank water. Though his success was limited, his work was widely reported in the U.S. and Europe.

Intelligent Whale

In 1864, another private endeavor constructed the Intelligent Whale in New York from a design by Scofield Merriman. It caught the attention of the Navy but was enmeshed in years of litigation before undergoing a single sea trial in 1872, the results of which failed to impress the Navy inspectors.

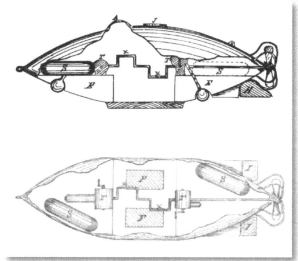

Marine Cigar

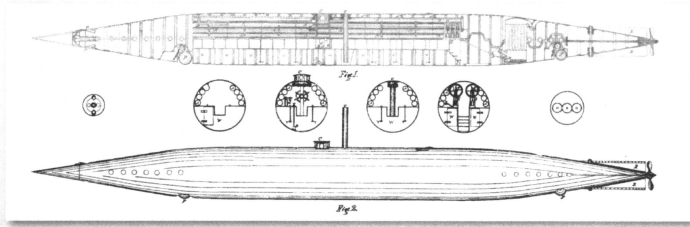

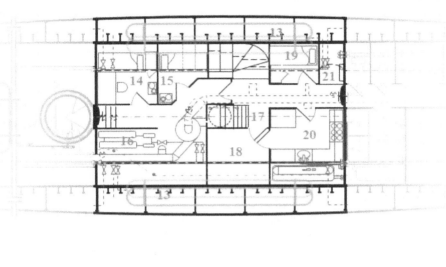

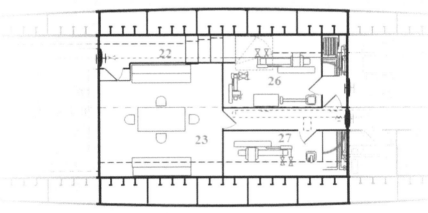

Third Compartment

INTERIOR LAYOUT – THIRD COMPARTMENT

"As soon as the narrow hatch was closed again over me, I was enveloped in profound darkness. My eyes, still drenched with the outside light, could make out nothing. I could tell that my naked feet were touching the rungs of an iron ladder. Firmly gripped by those men, Ned Land and Conseil were following me. At the foot of the ladder, a door opened and then closed behind us with a loud clang." p. 50

"...the cabin, which I now calculated, was about twenty feet by ten. As for its height, not even Ned, with his great stature, could reach the ceiling." p. 52

"Above the door there was an air vent through which masses of fresh air poured into our cabin." p. 59

"Following him [Captain Nemo], I passed through the door and found myself in a passageway, lighted by electricity, otherwise similar to a gangway on a more conventional vessel. After we walked ten meters or so, a second door opened before me, I then entered a dining room decorated and furnished in austere good taste. Tall oaken sideboards, inlaid with ebony, stood at the two ends of the room, their shelves sparkling with china, porcelain, and cut glass of incalculable value. Silver plate shone in the light shed by fixtures set in the ceiling, where fine painted designs tempered the glare. A table richly spread stood in the center of the hall." p. 67

"I was following Captain Nemo through corridors arranged for easy transit, and we arrived amidships. There I found myself at the base of a deep shaft between two watertight bulkheads. An iron ladder, clamped to a bulkhead, led upward. I asked the captain what the ladder was used for. 'It takes us to our dinghy,' he replied." p. 80

"After we passed by the well of the staircase that led to the platform, I looked into a cabin two meters long in which Conseil and Ned Land, seemingly enchanted with their food, were devouring it with gusto. Then a door led into the galley, three meters long, located between two large storage lockers. There electricity, more powerful and obedient than gas, did most of the cooking. Platinum griddles, connected to electric wires, gave off an even heat on the top of the stoves. Electricity also operated a distilling apparatus which, through evaporation, provided excellent drinking water." p. 80–81

"Then Captain Nemo led me to the galley where a large distilling machine was providing drinking water by means of evaporation." p. 329

"I walked to the central companionway, which led up to the platform, climbed the iron steps, passed through the open hatches, and found myself topside." p. 91

"Captain Nemo led me towards the central companionway. Halfway up he opened a door, walked through the upper gangway, and entered the wheelhouse which, as the reader already knows, rises at the end of the platform." p. 228

"Desperate, I rushed through the library, up the central companionway, through the upper gangway, and arrived beneath the dinghy. I climbed through the hatch and there were Conseil and Ned Land!" p. 384

"Ned Land seemed resolute, Conseil calm, but I felt so nervous I could not contain myself. We walked swiftly into the library, but the moment I opened the door leading to the central companionway, I heard the hatch closed sharply overhead. The Canadian rushed up the stairs, but I stopped him." p. 377

The arrangement of the dining room and the central stair, referred to in the text by the nautical term "companionway," is critical to defining the layout of the confusing third watertight compartment. The key interpretation leading to the plan shown is as follows: the door by which Aronnax exits the dining room is described as being in the rear (as he would have understood it at the time) of the room but not necessarily directly opposite the door from which they enter; a fact that Aronnax is careful to specify when they transition from the library to the salon. Moving from the dining room to the library they pass through a "double door," but a side-by-side type door is impractical for passing through a watertight bulkhead, so a better interpretation is two doors in sequence. Further support for this is provided later in the book when Verne uses the same term, "la double porte," as a shorthand to describe the diving chamber door arrangement, which is quite clearly two doors in sequence. In the exit from the dining room, nothing suggests that the two doors in sequence would have necessarily been facing each other. As shown in the plan, the small atrium at the base of the central staircase would have indeed felt like a double-door sort of arrangement as Aronnax understood the layout at that time.

As a rule, every attempt has been made to absolutely minimize the internal space devoted to corridors, as they are simply wasted space aboard submarines which, unlike surface ships, must strive for exceptionally high density. Though some have proposed that additional corridors must exist to circumvent the salon, such designs are overly complex, run counter to good submarine design, and are unnecessary in a part of the ship exclusively devoted to Captain Nemo's personal use. As shown, there is a very clean division between Captain Nemo's domain, which is entered via the relatively large and luxuriously spaced central steps, and the rest of the ship. The only other point of connection is the aft entrance to the dining room. This can be easily envisioned as the point of entry for the first mate, chief engineer, and some of the crew when they are invited to dine with Captain Nemo (an assumption on our part of a practice that existed before the arrival of Professor Aronnax). The built-in large oaken sideboards in the dining room disguise the lower curvature of the hull at deck height and allow

Figure 22: Early woodcut illustrations of the dining room and the ladder leading to the main hatch

the door to the library to go unnoticed until they rise to depart. They provide significant stowage for all the table settings and glassware on the *Nautilus*. Beneath the central stair and the short starboard passageway is the piping that connects to the forward trim tank and the electrical conduit from the battery. Bulkhead isolation valves are accessible under the deck plates.

The remaining arrangement of the third and fourth compartments is driven largely by the ten meter distance between the dining room and the door to the cell (assumed to be the crew's mess) and the dimensions of the cell itself. The sequence of spaces and their dimensions in the plan are consistent with the text, although some latitude exists in their arrangement. The two-deck division shown in compartment three and four is the optimal use of the cross-sectional area of a six meter diameter cylinder. It allows for two variable ballast tanks, mounted either side of centerline, in the lower part of the third watertight compartment, placing their buoyancy impact precisely amidships. Due to their length, transverse internal baffles are installed to inhibit destabilizing free surface effects. Mounted to the top of these tanks, port and starboard of the passageway, are the large ballast pumps that operate against sea pressure to discharge trim ballast overboard. An additional smaller trim pump primes the main pumps and can be used for movement of water within the *Nautilus* (see detail #7). These equipment spaces also accommodate spare parts and some machine shop equipment used to maintain the *Nautilus*. Immediately aft of the starboard auxiliary equipment space there is a ladder well, as Professor Aronnax describes, located between two bulkheads. Outboard is a hose reel holding 40 m of vulcanized India-rubber-lined, cotton-webbed fire hose, centrally located to service the entire ship. This type of hose construction was patented in 1821, and vulcanization in 1839, such that by 1870 this technology was making its way into domestic fire departments.[51] A hatch in the overhead leads into the hemispherical trunk that is mated to the dinghy. Unlike the design found in the *Plongeur*, Verne is quite clear that this access is in the side of the dinghy, "le flanc," and not the bottom. Doing so affords space to arrange two hatches so that both open against sea pressure, one protecting the dinghy and the other the *Nautilus*, when the two are not mated. The ladder that leads up to the dinghy extends downward into an access well that contains much of the piping, valves, and vents associated with the two potable water tanks and the sanitary waste tank located beneath the deck in compartment four. Two potable water tanks are provided so that one may be pressurized to provide a

continuous water supply while the other is filled from the still. Connections are provided to the distillation equipment located outboard in the galley, the hot water heater located outboard in the bathroom, the two toilets, and the ship's laundry.

The ability to produce fresh water aboard ships dates back to at least 1772, when Captain Cook recorded the use of a distillation apparatus aboard HMS *Resolution* as well as the crew's suspicion regarding "experimental water."[52] But the technology did not become practical until the advent of steam engines, which offered plentiful auxiliary heat to drive evaporation. In 1861, a distillation apparatus was installed in HMS *Warrior,* after which, the practice became widespread. By the end of the 19th century, distilling equipment such as Quiggin's Patent Evaporator were common in steam ships, whose boilers demanded sufficient quantities of makeup feedwater.[53] Distilling seawater, which boils at a temperature a few degrees higher than fresh water, had al-

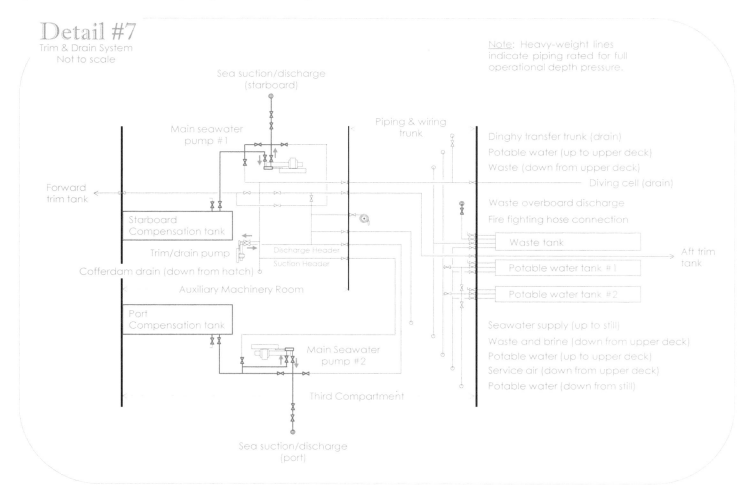

Detail #7
Trim & Drain System
Not to scale

Note: Heavy-weight lines indicate piping rated for full operational depth pressure.

ways required a great deal of energy, however, the advent of submarines necessitated an alternative means of powering the still. The first successful apparatus for distilling seawater on submarines was the Nelseco-Clarkson exhaust evaporator installed about 1916.[54] This evaporator used the exhaust from the main gasoline engines to heat the water to the boiling point. Since the operating conditions of the engine, and therefore the exhaust, varied, it was almost impossible to maintain a heat balance between the incoming feedwater and the condensing vapor. The quantity and quality of the fresh water varied with the operating conditions, and this system had the added disadvantage that it could operate at full capacity only when the submarine was running on the surface at high speeds. Shortly before World War II, the vapor compression still was developed that used electric heating coils and compressed the steam produced by boiling seawater, greatly increasing the efficiency of the process. This method was in widespread use in ships and submarines during the latter half of the 20th century until supplanted by flash-type evaporators, which heat water only to about 75°C and then evaporate the water in a vacuum.

The *Nautilus*, with its prodigious energy supply, utilizes electric heating coils to boil the seawater, and vapor compression is not assumed. The steam is collected and condensed conventionally in a heat exchanger that serves to pre-heat the incoming feedwater. The cooled distillate is then sent to the non-pressurized potable water tank for stowage and to allow the absorption of air to improve taste. The level of concentrating brine within the evaporator is maintained by an overflow whose outlet also passes through the heat exchanger to cool it, before draining to the sanitary waste tank for eventual discharge. The principal maintenance required for such equipment is the periodic removal of scale from the interior surfaces of the evaporator, which can be an arduous task that requires draining the contents. By using the ballast pump to drain the hot water-brine mix from the evaporator and inject it directly overboard, Captain Nemo is able to engineer their escape from the ice field.

On the upper deck, the galley, with its adjacent storeroom, is equipped with a sink and electric stove as de-

scribed. Such a stove would have been something of a novelty, since it was only in 1859 that George Simpson was awarded a U.S. patent for an "electro-heater" surface heated by a platinum-wire coil powered by batteries that in his words, would be useful to "warm rooms, boil water, cook victuals…"[55] Although vapor-compression commercial refrigeration had been patented in 1853 by Alexander Twining and was in use in the United States by 1856, any mention of such capability is conspicuously omitted in the description of the galley on board the *Nautilus*.[56] Rather, the daily retrieval of the fishing nets suggest a lack of refrigeration; accordingly, no such equipment is depicted in the drawings.

"These nets were always left trailing for several hours…" p. 122

"These various products of the ocean were lowered through the hatch and taken to the food lockers, some to be eaten fresh, the rest to be preserved." p. 122

"…several thousand kilos of meat were stored on board to be dried and preserved." p. 342

Opposite the galley, the small cabin provided for Ned Land and Conseil is, most logically, quarters formerly assigned to the cook. It would not be uncommon for this hardworking individual, with long and odd working hours, to be provided separate and better-than-average accommodations convenient to the galley. The small confines of this space require the lower bunk to be located quite close to the floor with a spare fold-down berth positioned above.

In considering the climb up the stairs from the library to the platform, the landing formed by the upper passageway deck could be regarded as, "halfway up," thus matching the described location of the door to the forward upper passageway that leads to the pilothouse. Despite the freedom Professor Aronnax has been given aboard the *Nautilus*, it is clear he seldom ventures into this space, enabling it to serve as a refuge for Captain Nemo during their time on board. In the small space over the central stair, a private bunk has been provided for Captain Nemo's use. Perhaps once the accommodations for a second mate, it now is in use as Captain Nemo's at-sea cabin, allowing him to remain close to the pilothouse when needed for extended periods. This is how he is able to go for days on board without being observed by Professor Aronnax—either out of operational necessity or simply a desire to retreat from his guests. As Captain Nemo's only apparent close peer on board, the mate has been provided a relatively large, single cabin, directly adjacent to the pilothouse.

An equipment space immediately forward of the ladder to the platform contains the large recirculation fans and the ship's air compressor. Outside air is drawn down an inlet plenum located under the stair in the superstructure, which serves as a kind of dorade box, and then through an induction hull valve. The fans direct air through a 12 inch diameter ventilation duct that runs in the overhead of the upper deck passageway all the way to the engine room, and also to one that runs beneath the ladder, into the overhead of the lower corridor, to the diving cell. From this distribution trunk, air enters the galley, crew staterooms, and the crew's mess through vents located above each doorway, as Aronnax has observed while imprisoned in the cell. A third ventilation duct runs forward past the pilothouse to exhaust in the ceiling of the dining room, library, and the wall of the salon. Isolation dampers are provided at each watertight bulkhead penetration. Positive ventilation pressure pushes air

inside the boat out the main hatch, which is used as an exhaust port. A total capacity of 900 cfm provides 30 cfm per person on board, a standard that exceeds the 10 cfm minimum in modern submarines and is consistent with building ventilation codes first established at the end of the 19th century.[57] This equipment space also contains the air compressor that can direct air to the internal reservoir forward of the pilothouse used to supply shipboard service needs, or to external reservoirs via the high-pressure air headers used to blow the main ballast tanks (detail #8). Unlike many modern submarines, the Nautilus does not appear to be equipped with the capability of using a large blower to direct air from the ship's atmosphere into the main ballast tanks. This would provide a means of expelling the water remaining in the ballast tanks below the waterline once a submarine has driven itself to the surface. This practice of performing a "low pressure blow" to achieve full freeboard conserves air stored in the reservoirs and expedites shipboard ventilation. However, nothing in the description of the Nautilus's surfacing evolution suggests this capability. In fact, Verne's prose suggests he held a more conventional conception of ballast tanks as discrete containers rather than trapped air spaces vented to the sea.

The Nautilus does not carry any CO_2 removal equipment as Professor Aronnax makes clear:

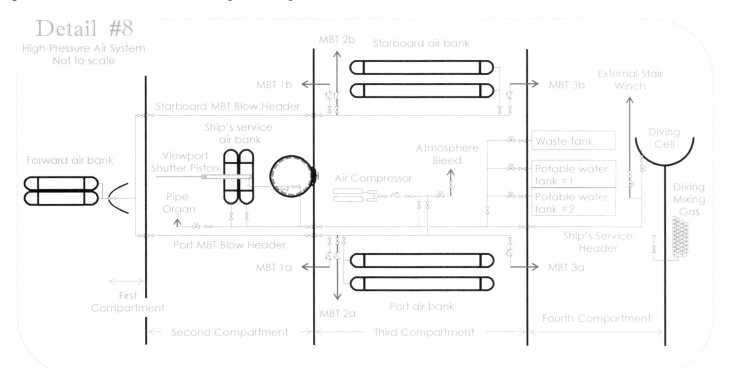

Detail #8
High-Pressure Air System
Not to scale

"...the carbon dioxide produced by our breathing had already pervaded every part of the ship. To absorb it we would have to fill containers with potassium hydroxide and shake them continually. But we had none of that chemical on board and nothing else could do the job." p. 328

This, despite submarine experiments since 1832 that demonstrated the ability of lime (CaO) dissolved in water to remove "carbonic acid" (CO_2) from air that was percolated through it. The reaction precipitates chalk ($CaCO_3$) and releases significant heat.[58] Caustic soda is similarly effective and came into use in early diving apparatus. Oxygen generation methods were also known. For example, heating a mixture of chlorate of potash ($KClO_3$) catalyzed with black oxide of manganese is a means of producing oxygen not unlike the chemistry used in oxygen candles aboard modern submarines, which often employ sodium perchlorate and iron powder.[59] Nonetheless, there is also no oxygen generating capability or storage tanks aboard the *Nautilus*. Although chapter 16 reports Captain Nemo bleeding "oxygen" into the ship, the term that appears in the original French is, "d'air pur" or "pure air," use of which will not improve their CO_2 concentration problem. Therefore, daily ventilation is necessary, as Captain Nemo confirms,

"'...we surface every morning to ventilate the ship in the open air.'" p. 81

Professor Aronnax attempts to calculate how long the atmosphere aboard can endure—a question which becomes acute when they find themselves trapped in the ice.

"'Each person needs, every hour, the oxygen contained in 100 liters of air. So in 24 hours, we each need the oxygen in 2,400 liters. The problem then is simply to calculate how many times 2,400 liters the *Nautilus* can hold...We get 625. In other words there is enough air in the *Nautilus* for 625 people for 24 hours.'" p. 287

This estimate of oxygen consumption is not unreasonable, but the conclusion is wrong. Depending upon fitness and activity level, the average adult male breathes

a volume of air equal to between 7 l/min (420 l/hr) at rest, and as much as 35 l/min (2,100 l/hr) walking briskly. Inhaled air is about 21% oxygen, and the air that is exhaled is about 16% oxygen, so about 5% of the volume of air is consumed in each breath and converted to CO_2. This equates to an oxygen requirement of about 21 l/hr at rest, or 105 l/hr walking. However, the limiting factor, which Aronnax fails to consider, is not the oxygen consumption but rather the CO_2 production. A moderately stressed or active person could be expected to produce some 48 liters of CO_2 per hour, though it is reasonable to assume that a disciplined submarine crew, even in an emergency, could maintain activity rates as low as 24 l/hr. Prolonged exposure to CO_2 concentrations above 4% produces headache, vision and hearing disturbances, and drowsiness leading to unconsciousness. If we use Verne's internal volume of 1,500,000 liters, the maximum endurance of the atmosphere is 2,500 man-hrs, or for the twenty-six aboard the *Nautilus*, four days. Our design for the inhabitable volume of the *Nautilus* is 1,310,000 liters, and equipment installed within this volume further reduces the quantity of air available to breathe. In modern submarines, this so-called "floodable volume" within the pressure hull ranges from 75-80%.[60] The *Nautilus* is relatively spacious, especially the forward end, so using a more generous value of 85% reduces the available atmosphere to 1,113,500 l. This gives a maximum endurance of 1,855 man-hrs, or for the twenty-six aboard the *Nautilus*, three days. During the period when they are trapped in the ice, approximately half of the crew is working outside the ship, and so the endurance could be stretched to six days. This is consistent with the timeline for escaping the ice bank in which Professor Aronnax becomes the first to succumb to unconsciousness on the sixth day.

For routine operations, with crew activity producing CO_2 at an average rate of about 24 l/hr per man, ventilation of the atmosphere every 24 hours is necessary to maintain CO_2 below 1.5%. This is a reasonable upper limit based on crew comfort and performance, and it requires good internal air circulation as the distribution of personnel within the *Nautilus* is markedly uneven. These calculations suggest that our estimate of crew size and internal equipment density are approximately correct.[61]

Submarine Development

Spurred by the need to counter Union naval dominance, Confederates undertook a flurry of submersible development. The Pioneer, *designed and built by James McClintock and Baxter Watson, was the first submarine to be granted a letter of marque in 1862, though the vessel never saw action. Their next design, the* American Diver, *attempted an attack in 1863 and was later swamped in rough seas. The* Hunley, *constructed in 1863, sank twice during trials killing two crews before sinking the USS Housatonic in the world's first successful submarine attack.*

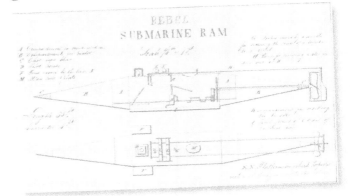

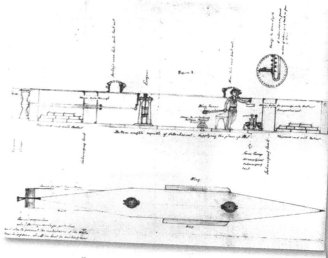

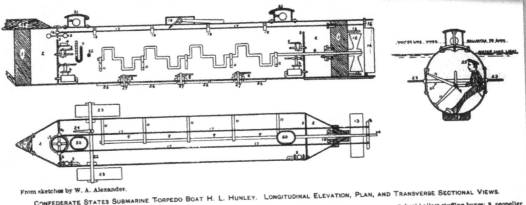

From sketches by W. A. Alexander.

CONFEDERATE STATES SUBMARINE TORPEDO BOAT H. L. HUNLEY. LONGITUDINAL ELEVATION, PLAN, AND TRANSVERSE SECTIONAL VIEWS.

1. The bow and stern castings; 2, water-ballast tanks; 3, tank bulkheads; 4, compass; 5, sea cocks; 6, pumps; 7, mercury gauge; 8, keel-ballast stuffing boxes; 9, propeller shaft and cranks; 10, stern bearing and gland; 11, shaft braces; 12, propeller; 13, wrought ring around propeller; 14, rudder; 15, steering wheel; 16, steering lever; 17, steering rods; 18, rod braces; 19, air box; 20, hatchways; 21, hatch covers; 22, shaft of side fins; 23, side fins; 24, shaft lever; 25, one of the crew turning propeller shaft; 26, cast-iron keel ballast; 27, bolts; 28, butt end of torpedo boom.

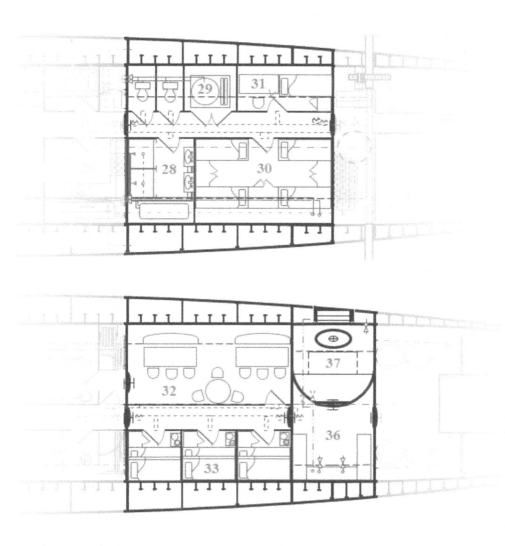

Fourth Compartment

INTERIOR LAYOUT – FOURTH COMPARTMENT

"At the foot of the ladder, a door opened and then closed behind us with a loud clang." p. 50

"Following him [Captain Nemo], I passed through the door and found myself in a passageway, lighted by electricity, otherwise similar to a gangway on a more conventional vessel. After we walked ten meters or so, a second door opened before me, I then entered a dining room..." p. 67

"An adjoining [to the kitchen] bathroom, comfortably arranged, supplied with hot and cold running water. Next came the crew's quarters, five meters long. But the door was closed, and I couldn't study the accommodations, which might have told me how many men it took to run the Nautilus." p. 81

"Captain Nemo conducted me to the stern of the Nautilus, into a cabin near the crew's quarters." p. 173

Verne is never clear what purpose their initial confinement cell might serve, however as it is the largest space in the crew's portion of the Nautilus, it is most logically the crew's mess. Although it seems sparsely furnished for that function, conceivably some tables and chairs could have been removed prior to its use as a holding cell. Although two doors to the cell are not specifically described, their entry via an iron ladder and a watertight door, and Aronnax's exit with Captain Nemo into a relatively featureless well-lit passageway, suggest that there must be two means of access. Thus the ladder, the dinghy access (and therefore the dinghy), the crew's mess, and the location of the third watertight bulkhead are mutually dependent. The bathroom is described as adjoining the galley, and separately accessed toilets have been provided across the passageway from the showers and sinks to improve the access to and efficiency in using all of the facilities that are shared by the entire crew. A 400 liter electric hot water heater occupies the space outboard of the bathroom where headroom is restricted. Adjacent to the toilets is a space housing the ship's laundry machine. Machinery design of that period would have included a wash basin with a mechanically assisted wringer. The overhead of the passageway in this compartment provides stowage space, adjacent to the ventilation duct, for harpoons used to hunt the dugong, and perhaps a boathook as well. Finally, this compartment provides berthing spaces for a majority of the crew. On the upper deck a bunkroom with ten bunks (three high inboard, two high outboard) and clothing lockers is situated. Although never specifically mentioned by Professor

Aronnax, we have assumed the existence of a chief engineer, who, like the first mate, can be considered one of the ship's "officers" and thus something of a peer to Captain Nemo. Similar to the mate, a separate cabin has been provided immediately adjacent to the engine room. On the lower deck, three small staterooms are each equipped with three bunks, a clothing locker, and a washbasin for the more senior members of the crew. One of these cabins is where Aronnax is brought to tend to the injured crew member.

Scrutiny of the accommodations raises the subject of crew size. Verne is deliberately vague about the exact size and composition of the Nautilus's crew. The largest number observed at any one time by Aronnax is "vingtaine matelots," or approximately twenty sailors (sometimes translated as "a number" or "a score"), not including Captain Nemo. Later in the voyage, after two crewmembers have been killed, Aronnax observes,

"some fifteen of the Nautilus's crewmen were surrounding their captain." p. 375

The first mate is not mentioned among them. Since an additional three or four crewmembers almost certainly would have been below on watch in the pilothouse and engine room, a crew of twenty-two seems reasonable. A nominal proposal for their division is as follows:

1x first mate, 1x chief engineer, 1x cook
4x helmsmen, 12x engineer/auxiliary-men
3x kitchen assistants/stewards

We have assumed a four-section watch rotation, which is more practical to sustain indefinitely as a lifestyle than a three-section watch often used on warships. Each watch requires a helmsman in the pilothouse, an auxiliary-man to operate equipment and valves in compartment three, and two engineers in compartment five. One engineer responds to propulsion commands from the pilothouse and maintains ship's angle with the stern planes, while the other is a roving watch to operate and maintain the propulsion equipment. For each crewmember, this creates a daily schedule of six hours on watch, six hours performing maintenance tasks, four hours free and eight hours for sleep. The cook works a single long day shift, assisted by the three stewards who work an eighteen-hour day split into overlapping watches for meal preparation. As is typical on submarines, other crewmembers would assist the kitchen staff with the setup, cleanup, and provisioning tasks.

The origins of Captain Nemo's crew are never specified, but Professor Aronnax observes that they are of diverse ethnicities.

> "These seamen obviously hailed from many different countries, but I surmised they were all European in origin. I thought I could recognize some Irishmen, some Frenchmen, a few Slavs, a native of Greece or Crete." p. 121

It is curious that there appear to be no natives of India, Captain Nemo's homeland, among them. Perhaps the crew composition reflects Captain Nemo's long educational sojourn in Europe during the tumultuous and widespread uprisings of 1832 and 1848. It may also reflect a vestige of Verne's original intent for Captain Nemo to be a Polish revolutionary, or he may be merely attempting to improve the connection with his mostly European audience. Lacking a common language, and perhaps to further divorce themselves from the civilized world, they have adopted a language of their own invention. For Verne, having the crew speak an unintelligible language focuses the drama on Captain Nemo and his guests and simplifies his writing challenge. But this also reflects Verne's own interest with the idea, relatively new at that time, of a universal constructed language, which is given expression by Conceil.

> "Now we see the disadvantage of not knowing many languages, or is it the disadvantage of not having one universal language?'" p. 55

The first such language, Solresol, was developed by François Sudre, whose book, *Langue Musicale Universelle*, was published in 1866, though it had been publicized for some years beforehand. Verne became a strong proponent for an artificial international language, and in the 1890s would serve as a chairman of a local Espe-

 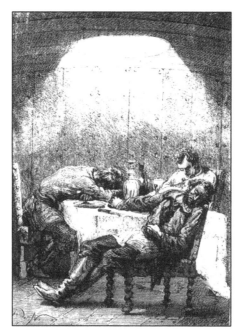 

Figure 23: An aft compartment passageway and the holding cell

rantist group.[62] The development of Volap□k and Esperanto at the end of the 19th century marked the peak of the constructed language movement, which faded in the face of the world wars of the 20th century.

Little else about the crew makes an impression on Professor Aronnax, but perhaps his limited observations and lack of engagement with them is due to distinctions in class. Regardless, the crew appear to be a rather grim lot, mostly occupied with their duties and not given to emotional expression, even in the most dire of circumstances. Presumably they are survivors or refugees of various unsuccessful rebellions against imperialism. When they visit the Coral Cemetery in the vicinity of 105°E / 15°S, the presence of several graves suggests that others among them have been previously lost. It is possible that their composition is not static and that from time to time, Captain Nemo replenishes losses with new freedom fighters fleeing persecution, with whom he maintains contact around the world. If true, then the Greek diver encountered off of Crete provides an example of another potential future crewmember. The extent of this revolutionary network, and indeed, much of Captain Nemo's politically motivated mission, is kept carefully concealed from his guests. However, given Captain Nemo's in-finite wealth and propensity to support struggles for liberation, it is not inconceivable that he could find a ready supply of recruits to man the *Nautilus*, despite the isolation and austerity of their existence on board.

Ironically, Captain Nemo's isolation from current events causes him to miss his greatest opportunity to strike at his foe during his transit of the Red Sea. At the time of this unhurried passage, which occurs over the course of February 5–10, 1868, the British had assembled hundreds of ships in Annesley Bay. They were supporting the expedition to Abyssinia led by General Sir Robert Napier to recover hostages and punish Ethiopian Emperor Tewodros. It seems incredible that operating both surfaced and submerged across the breadth of the Red Sea, the *Nautilus* does not encounter British vessels, warships or otherwise, to prompt an attack. A further irony is that during this exercise in imperial hubris which would have so riled Captain Nemo, the Commodore of the fleet anchored in the bay, Leopold Heath, was formulating a plan to end the African slave trade that emanated from Zanzibar. It would prove to be controversial, but ultimately effective, as the most concerted maritime effort untaken by England to stem the trade in slaves; a mission surely aligned with Captain Nemo's ideals.[63]

Submarine Development

Individual diving suits complemented diving bell development during this period. Diving armor developed by Captain William Taylor was in use for marine salvage from 1838 to 1858. It was improved upon by diver James Whipple who added an escape valve for exhaled air, thus eliminating the need for a second surface hose.

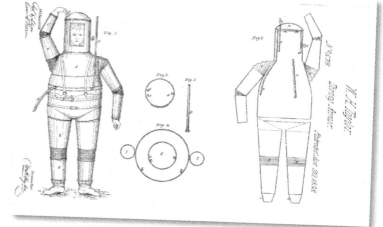

DIVING CELL

"We came to a cell near the engine room, where we were to put on our underwater walking suits." p. 108

"The cell was, properly speaking, both the arsenal and the wardrobe of the *Nautilus*. A dozen deep-sea diving outfits were hanging on the walls, awaiting the hikers." p. 109

"I felt myself being propelled into another room contiguous to the wardrobe. My companions followed, pushed and pulled like myself. I heard a door with watertight seals close and we were enveloped in deep darkness. In a few minutes, I could hear a sharp hissing and felt coldness mounting from my knees to my chest. Obviously someone inside the ship had opened a stopcock and allowed seawater to overrun us and soon fill that cell. A second door, placed in the side of the *Nautilus*, opened and a dusky light fell over us. A second later we were treading the bottom of the sea." p. 110

"The double door was opened and, accompanied by Captain Nemo and a dozen of the crew, we set foot on the solid seafloor where the *Nautilus* rested ten meters down." p. 175

"'We use the Rouquayrol-Denayrouze apparatus...which I have perfected for our special use, permitting you to venture into these new physiological conditions without suffering any organic disorders. It consists of a tank made of thick iron in which I store air under a pressure of 50 atmospheres. This tank is strapped on your back like a soldier's pack. The upper part of the tank is a compartment from which the air, regulated by a bellows mechanism, can be released only at the proper pressure. In the Rouquayrol apparatus that has been in use, two India-rubber hoses go from that upper compartment to a mask that covers the man's nose and mouth; one hose is for breathing in fresh air, the other for exhaling stale air; the tongue closes off one or the other according to the man's needs. But for myself, since I have to move around under considerable pressure on the sea floor, the mask would not suffice. I have to protect my head inside a copper sphere, such as divers use, and so I fix those two hoses, for inhaling and exhaling, into that sphere.'" p. 105–106

"'...and the *Nautilus's* pumps enable me to store air under considerable pressure; I can put enough breathable air in the tanks of my diving apparatus to last nine or ten hours.'" p. 106

"'While the breathing equipment is carried on the back, the Ruhmkorff is attached to the belt. It's composed of a Bunsen battery that I activate not with potassium dichromate but with sodium. An induction coil collects the electricity that is produced and conducts it to a special lantern. In this lantern, there is a glass tube in the form of a spiral that contains only a residue of carbon dioxide. When the apparatus is turned on, this gas becomes luminous and gives off a continuous whitish light. Thus equipped, I can breathe and can see perfectly well.'" p. 106

"...two of the crew helped us to dress in these heavy, waterproof garments, made of seamless India rubber and designed expressly to withstand considerable pressure... It consisted of jacket and pants. The pants terminated in thick boots, with heavy lead soles. The fabric of the jacket was stretched over copper mail that protected the chest from the crushing pressure and allowed the lungs to function freely; the sleeves terminated in supple gloves that made it easy to work with the hands." p. 109

"The jacket terminated in a collar of threaded copper, into which the metallic sphere was screwed. Three holes, covered with thick glass, allowed me to look in any direction simply by turning my head inside the copper sphere." p. 110

The diving cell is a transverse cylindrical watertight section centered on the fourth bulkhead for strength. The hyperbaric chamber is the starboard half of this cylinder, segregated by a hemispherical end section. This construction provides the maximum resistance to pressure to allow for egress at the depths described (300 m at Atlantis, 350 m in the ice caves). The wide shallow steps are designed with the cumbersome diving suits in mind and reduce the angle that the egress ramp must make to reach the ocean floor when the *Nautilus* is bottomed. A portion of the outer hull serves as the ramp, which is operated by an overhead, air powered winch. The chamber is flooded from sea and drained to the variable ballast system, which can compensate for the additional 24 t of water weight. The location of this added weight is just within the capacity of the trim system to balance, assuming careful attention is given to tank levels beforehand, however, as a practical matter the chamber is typically only flooded when the *Nautilus* is bottomed. Equalization with outside pressure is done locally in the chamber. After prolonged dives the chamber can be used for decompressing saturated personnel, which in modern saturation diving is safely performed at a rate of 15 m per day, making the inaccuracies of the diving experience reported in Professor Aronnax's memoir apparent.

The port side of the diving cell affords a stowage area beneath the deck, which is an open grate construction to allow fresh water, used to wash down equipment following a dive, to drain to the bilge. This area also has racks to store at least sixteen diving apparatus (the maximum number reported in simultaneous use) as well as an unspecified number of rifles.

The Rouquayrol-Denayrouze diving suit was patented in 1864 as the first diving suit that could supply air to the diver on demand through the use of a regulator (or "bellows mechanism") until rediscovered in 1943 by Jacques Cousteau. Although it incorporated a small air tank that could hold air at 40 atmospheres, permitting independent operations for perhaps thirty minutes at ten meters of depth, in practical use this reservoir was continuously resupplied by a surface-tended air hose.[64] The apparatus won a gold medal at the 1867 World's Fair that Verne attended. Among the modifications Captain Nemo has made, is exchanging the Rouquayrol-Denayrouze "mask" for a closed helmet of the sort developed by Auguste Siebe around 1840. This helmet design also incorporated check valves that made it unnecessary for the diver to use his tongue to control incoming and outgoing air. As in modern hard-hat diving, the helmet makes a hard connection to a breast plate that is part of the diving suit torso or jacket. Lead weights, incorporated into the boots and hung from the belt, ensure negative buoyancy during the dive.

In order to achieve dive durations anywhere near nine or ten hours, we must assume that Captain Nemo has pioneered closed circuit rebreather technology. At the time Verne was writing, a Belgian professor had designed an early rebreather consisting of a large back-mounted oxygen tank with a working pressure of about 13.1 atmospheres, and two scrubbers containing sponges soaked in caustic soda. It was exhibited in Paris in 1878. By the turn of the century, Oxylithe (a form of sodium peroxide or sodium dioxide) had been

Figure 24: A Rouquayrol-Denayrouze diving suit (left) and original woodcut illustration of the diving cell aboard the Nautilus *(right)*

invented, which emits oxygen as it absorbs carbon dioxide in a rebreather's scrubber. It was used in the first filming of *Twenty Thousand Leagues Under the Sea* in 1907.[65] Rebreathers recycle the exhaled oxygen and inert gases and permit much longer dives for a specific volume of breathing gas carried.

The depth record for diving on compressed air is 155 m, an extremely dangerous practice due to the extreme risk of both nitrogen narcosis and oxygen toxicity that result from the high partial pressures of those gases at depth. To even attempt dives at the extreme depths recorded in the text, an inert gas, typically helium, must be inserted into the mix to reduce the proportions of oxygen and nitrogen and their associated effects. The record for such Trimix scuba diving is 1,000 ft, however high-pressure nervous syndrome often becomes incapacitating below 150 m.[66] Helium is unlikely to be Captain Nemo's diving gas since it was only first detected in 1868 by French astronomer Jules Janssen, and it wasn't until the turn of the century that fractional distillation of natural gas was able to produce it in quantity.[67] An alternative is to use hydrogen in place of helium. Although the first reported use of hydrogen seems to be by Antoine Lavoisier, who had guinea pigs breathe it, the actual first use of this gas in diving is usually attributed to trials by the Swedish engineer Arne Zetterström in 1945. Recently, Comex, a French diving company, developed procedures allowing dives between 500 m and 700 m in depth, while breathing gas mixtures of hydreliox (hydrogen-oxygen-nitrogen) or hydrox (hydrogen-oxygen), however, symptoms of hydrogen narcosis became a factor at depths deeper than 300 m.[68] Hydrogen and its production via electrolysis of water was well known in Captain Nemo's time, and although he claims in the book to not produce oxygen on board for the ship's atmosphere using this technique, he would need a source of hydrogen for his diving gas mixture. Storage cylinders for this diving gas are provided in the upper platform of the engine room and piped into the diving cell immediately below.

> "'...this gun doesn't shoot ordinary bullets, it shoots little glass capsules invented by the Austrian chemist Leinebroch. And I have a large supply. These glass capsules are sheathed in steel and weighted with lead. They are veritable little Leyden jars charged with high-voltage electricity. At the slightest impact they discharge, and the animal, no matter how large or strong, falls dead. Furthermore, these capsules are no bigger than number 4 shot, and the chamber of any ordinary gun could hold ten of them.'" p. 108

The compressed air rifles carried by the *Nautilus's* crew fire an innovative electric projectile. Leyden jars were the first capacitors, created by lining the inside and outside of a glass jar with foil; the glass forming the dielectric between the two charged metal surfaces. Invented independently in 1745 by German cleric Ewald Georg von Kleist and by Dutch scientist Pieter van Musschenbroek of Leiden (Leyden), the technology would have been well known to readers of that time, who would have recognized the ability of such devices to store a significant charge, and discharge it at will.[69] The capacitance of such a device increases with a higher voltage applied, a thinner dielectric, and a larger surface area of the foil. The "capsules" invented by Leinebroch (a chemist evidently lost to history) are the size of number 4 buckshot, or approximately 0.24 in (6.1 mm), and so their maximum capacity for storing charge is surely limited. Captain Nemo implies that each of his shells holds ten such pellets, which would certainly magnify their effect. How deadly such a projectile would be is not obvious, since it is not the voltage but rather the current and its path through the body that determines lethality. The modern Taser works on a similar principle. Two probes, propelled by compressed nitrogen, deliver high voltage at a low current, which overstimulates sensory and motor nerves producing involuntary long muscle contractions. This stuns and physically incapacitates the victim but is seldom as deadly as Captain Nemo describes. Although Tasers currently in production require electric wires to conduct the charge from a source within the gun, research projects are underway to develop a self-contained projectile that functions exactly as Captain Nemo describes.

Submarine Development

In 1878, George Garrett, a British curate, constructed two submarines named Resurgam (Latin for "I shall rise again"). Propelled underwater by stored steam energy, neither was successful, but they inspired a collaboration with Swedish industrialist Thorsten Nordenfelt. Together they built a series of larger steam-powered submarines that were sold to Greece, Turkey, and Russia, though operationally they proved worthless. By contrast, a Spanish naval officer named Isaac Peral convinced authorities to build his sophisticated design for a submarine. It was electrically powered, pioneered modern cruciform control surfaces, and, in 1888, launched the first submarine torpedo. Though highly successful, it ran afoul of bureaucratic politics and failed to gain acceptance.

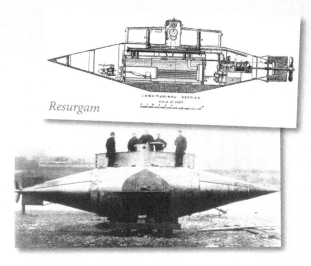

Resurgam

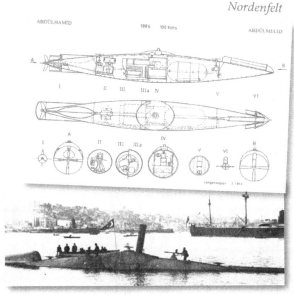

Nordenfelt

Peral

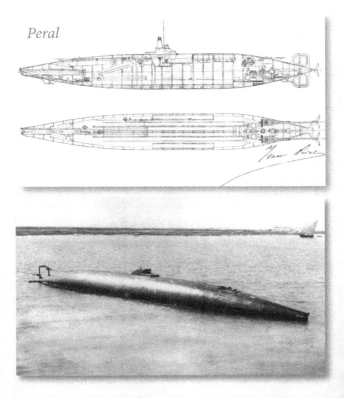

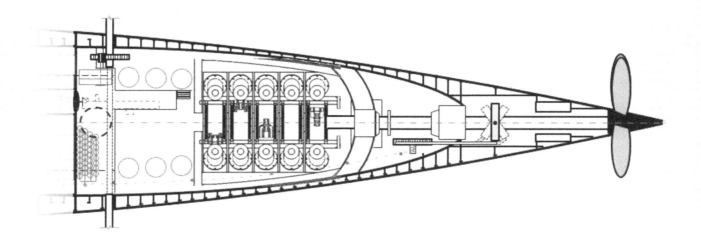

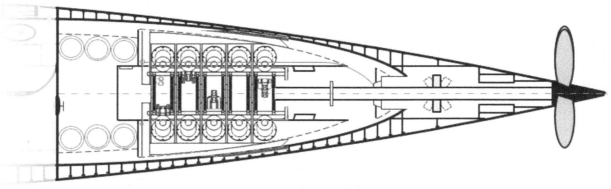

Fifth Compartment

INTERIOR LAYOUT – FIFTH COMPARTMENT

"Separating the crew's quarters from the engine room was a fourth watertight bulkhead. A door opened and I found myself in the compartment where Captain Nemo—obviously a first-class engineer—had set up his locomotive apparatus. Evenly lighted, this engine room was at least twenty meters long. It was divided, by function, into two sections: the first enclosed the equipment for generating electricity, the second the mechanism for transmitting this power to the propeller. I was surprised to sniff a strange odor, absolutely *sui generis*, which pervaded this compartment. Captain Nemo noticed my concern. 'That,' he reassured me, 'is a gas produced by our use of sodium. It's only a slight inconvenience. Anyhow, we surface every morning to ventilate the ship in the open air.'" p. 81

"Meanwhile, I was examining the *Nautilus's* machinery with impatient curiosity. 'You see,' the Captain said, 'I use Bunsen cells instead of Ruhmkorff cells, which aren't powerful enough. You use fewer Bunsen cells but they are large and strong. Experience shows that they're better. The electricity I generate here is conducted aft. There large electromagnets actuate a special system of levers and gears that in turn transmit the power to the propeller shaft.'" p. 81

"There was still a mystery here, but I didn't insist on exploring. How could electricity produce such power? What source of energy was he really tapping? Was it in the exorbitant voltage developed by a new kind of induction coil? Had he worked out a new transmission system, a secret system of levers that could step up the power infinitely?" p. 83

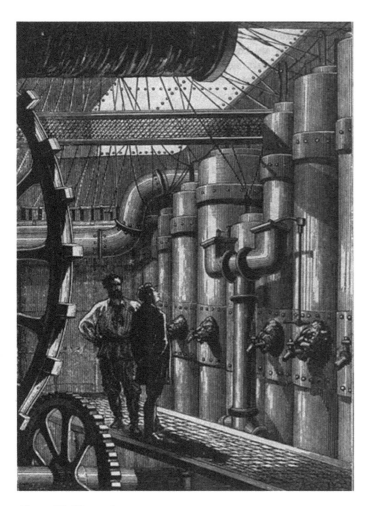

Figure 25: The engine room

Beyond the fourth watertight compartment lies the engine room. Professor Aronnax estimates the space is at least 20 m in length; as drawn it is 15 m. This is a result of the conscious decision to place the watertight bulkhead at the hull geometry transition point and to maintain the spheroid hull geometry symmetric forward and aft. Thus, shortening the pressure hull forward to provide for separate air reservoir tanks in the bow results in a corresponding reduction of space in the engine room. This deviation is justified as follows. Professor Aronnax is making his estimate from the engine room upper mezzanine just inside the hatch. This is the largest space on the ship, it is densely packed with equipment, and it tapers dramatically toward the stern, making a precise estimate difficult. Although the design results in a "loss" of 5 m of equipment space in the engine room, we have chosen to place the seawater pumps, fans, and air compressors, which are referred to in the text but whose location is not specified, in logical spaces amidships. Doing so effectively relocates the equivalent of 5 m of equipment from the engineering spaces. Not only is this functionally more efficient, but it further assists with weight distribution and pushes the ratio of equipment space to living/payload space to a higher and therefore more realistic number (see table 2). In modern submarines, typical ratios of equipment space to living/payload space are significantly higher (~55%) than would be the case on the *Nautilus* if we are to believe that all equipment is located solely in the engine room. For this reason, locating auxiliary equipment outside the engine room makes for a more realistic apportionment of space.

In the mezzanine, to starboard, is the electrical switchboard. The watch-stander here controls the electrical distribution and responds to engine orders from the pilothouse. In addition, he is responsible for maintaining angle on the ship by controlling the stern planes, which are geared to the hand wheel mounted to the front of this station. Six power generation cylinders dominate the high bay area, which is separated

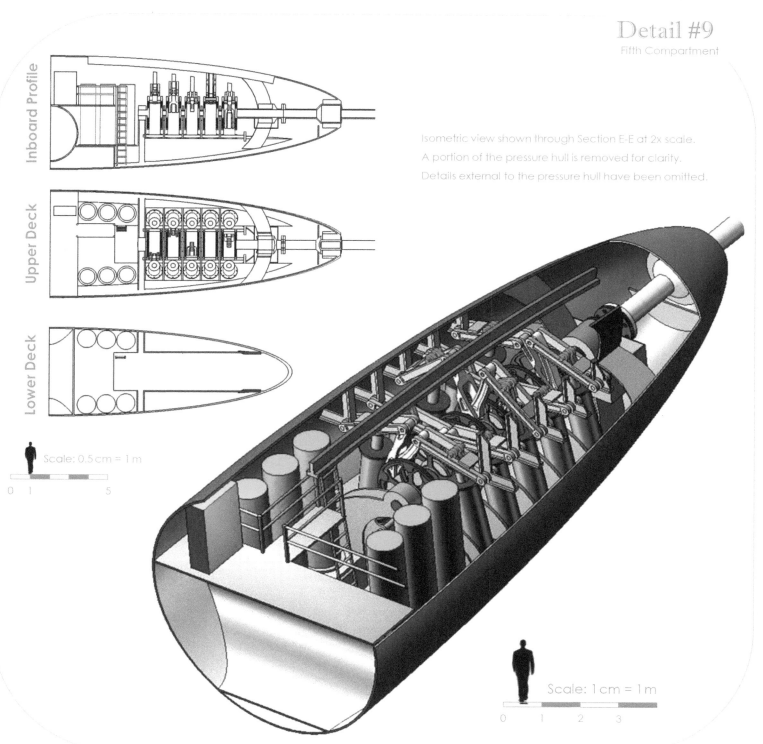

Inboard Profile

Upper Deck

Lower Deck

Scale: 0.5 cm = 1 m
0   1   5

Detail #9
Fifth Compartment

Isometric view shown through Section E-E at 2x scale.
A portion of the pressure hull is removed for clarity.
Details external to the pressure hull have been omitted.

Scale: 1 cm = 1 m
0   1   2   3

from the propulsion engine by the crank shaft forward support frame and the flywheel. A passage below allows access farther aft. The shaft is supported by six radial frames that transmit axial thrust of the propeller to the hull via a thrust bearing. A lubrication oil stowage tank is located under the main thrust bearing. Beneath the lignum vitae water lubricated bearing in the stern tube is a collection sump that gravity drains to the aft trim tank. This tank, vented to ship's atmosphere, extends under the electro-magnetic drive cylinder mounts and engine room lower deck. An overhead rail enables the hoist to move large, heavy components and position them directly underneath the hull plug. Each of the major engine assemblies (solenoids, gear linkages, shaft segments, etc.) are sized to fit through this access port or can be broken down into smaller parts that permit extraction. Not shown in detail #9 are two transformers (referred to as Ruhmkorff coils) that are suspended from the overhead just aft of the mezzanine.

Curiously, the main propulsion engine on the *Nautilus* is not a rotating electric motor. This despite the fact that English scientist Michael Faraday had established the principle of the rotating motor by 1825, and Thomas Davenport had patented a direct-current motor with all its essentials — rotating coils, a commutator, and brushes — in 1837. By mid-century, several rotary motor vehicles had been demonstrated in both Europe and America, but instead, the described design for the prime mover on the *Nautilus* emerges as the electrical analog of a reciprocating steam engine, with large electromagnets replacing conventional pistons.[70] Such an axial reciprocal engine was also chosen by Dr. Charles Page in the demonstration of an electric locomotive that traveled 10 miles and reached 19 mph in 1851. Although the trial was plagued with electrical insulation breakdowns and cracked batteries, it received a widely-read positive write-up in *Scientific American*.[71] It was the most powerful electrical engine of its time, and its similarity to large maritime engines, such as those of the SS *Great Eastern*, may have further helped make the solenoid motor appear more credible than the relatively immature rotary motors of that period.

Detail #10a

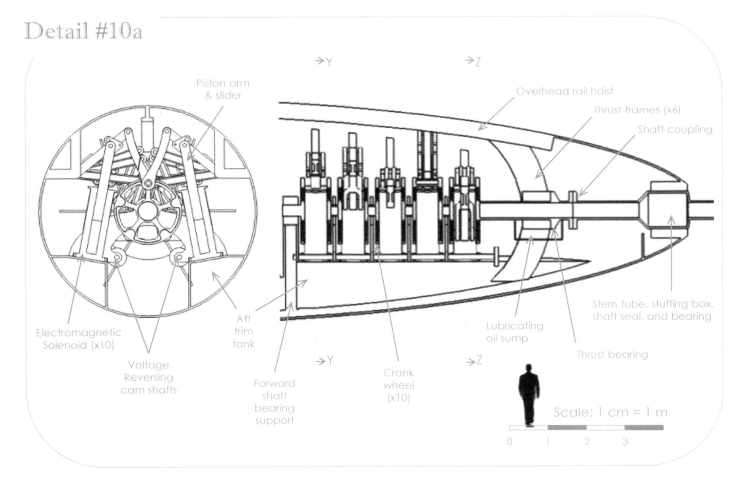

Scale: 1 cm = 1 m

Detail #10b
Engine

Direction of rotation

Section Y-Y

Section Z-Z

Engine cross sections depict sequential rotation positions of the shaft and drive levers through one complete cycle.

Reversing solenoid polarity alternatively attracts/repels the magnetic piston generating force on the upward and downward strokes.

The pistons transmit force via sliders to segmented drive linkages that are connected to five pairs of drive wheels in five clocked positions.

The drive wheels are connected to the shaft, which is supported by a forward bearing and a thrust bearing that transmits propulsive force of the screw to the hull.

Scale: 1 cm = 1 m

0   1   2   3

1

2

3

4

5

POWER SOURCE

"'There is a powerful agent, obedient, rapid, facile, which can be put to any use and reigns supreme on board my ship. It does everything. It illuminates our ship, it warms us, it is the soul of our mechanical apparatus. This agent is—electricity.'"

"'Professor,' the captain responded, 'my electricity is not the usual electricity.'" p. 78

"'…I do not want to use the same metals that landsmen use. I want to get my electricity from the sea itself.'" p. 78

"'You know what seawater is composed of. In 1,000 grams you find 96.5 percent water and about 2.66 percent of sodium chloride. Then, in smaller quantities, magnesium chloride, potassium chloride, magnesium bromide, sulfate of magnesia, calcium sulfate, calcium carbonate. So you know then that sodium chloride in there is good proportions. And it's that sodium that I extract from seawater, that sodium that composes my electric cells…'" p. 78

"'I don't use batteries, at least not for the extraction process. I use heat from coal in the earth.'" p. 79

"'[the Nautilus] needs electricity for power, batteries to produce the electricity, sodium for the batteries, coal to make the sodium, and coalfields from which to extract the coal.'" p. 272

"'These mines extend out under the waves like the coalfields at Newcastle. My men get into their diving suits, take pick and shovel, *go into the water* to extract the coal—making me independent of mines on dry land. When I burn this coal to manufacture sodium, the smoke rising from this mountain's crater make it look as if the volcano is still active.'" p. 272

"'Some day you'll see how we do it, professor… Just remember one thing: I owe all to the ocean. It produces electricity, and electricity gives the Nautilus heat, light, movement, and in a word, life.'" p. 79

The *Nautilus* represents an incarnation of the all-electric ship that modern submarine design has been slowly evolving toward. Electricity provides the means to light, heat, and propel the vessel as well as the power to distill fresh water, cook food, and communicate orders. Interestingly, Verne did not foresee the electro-mechanical actuation of control surfaces or valves that is extensively employed in modern submarines. Despite this omission, the use of electricity aboard the *Nautilus* is pervasive and advanced for its time. But what source generates this vast electrical power?

Although some hasty writers have wrongly portrayed the *Nautilus* as "nuclear-powered," the actual source for her vast reserves of electricity is described as a hugely scaled-up elaboration of a well-known 19th-century primary battery, the Bunsen cell. Invented in 1841 by German physicist Robert Bunsen, it uses a carbon cathode in nitric acid and a zinc anode in dilute sulfuric acid, with a porous separator between the liquids.[72] The overall reaction is given as:

$$Zn(s) + H_2SO_4(aq) + 2HNO_3 \square ZnSO_4 + 2H_2O + 2NO_2(g)$$

However, this cell would have been impractical on a submarine because of the necessity of venting the pungent NO_2 fumes. In addition to being noxious, nitrogen dioxide is highly reactive and as an oxidizer it will combust, sometimes explosively. Interestingly, if heated to 150°C it decomposes and could be a means for producing oxygen.

One alternative, developed in 1842 by German physicist Johann Poggendorff, would be the dichromate cell. Although it adds the complication of requiring a supply of sulfuric acid and potassium dichromate, it eliminates the production of NO_2 by substituting the reduction of the dichromate anion for the reduction of nitric acid at the cathode, and in the process increases the net standard potential of the cell from 1.72 V to 2.09 V.[73]

$$3Zn(s) + 7H_2SO_4(aq) + K_2(Cr_2O_7)(aq) \square$$
$$3Zn(SO_4)(aq) + K_2(SO_4)(aq) + Cr_2(SO_4)_3(aq) + 7H_2O(l)$$

Captain Nemo's substitution of sodium for zinc would produce a very energetic and perhaps even explosive reaction. But in describing his modification of the traditional cell chemistry, he hints at something different from a battery.

> "'Mixed with mercury, sodium forms an amalgam that takes the place of zinc in Bunsen batteries. The mercury is never consumed, only the sodium is used up, and the sea resupplies me with that. Moreover, I can tell you, sodium batteries are more powerful. Their electric motive force is twice that of zinc batteries.'" p. 78

This sounds much more like an early sodium-amalgam-oxygen fuel cell that was secretly developed in the 1950s for potential Navy submarine application.[74] In such a system, a sodium amalgam, introduced at the top of a vertical plate or cylinder, flows down the surface within a saltwater electrolyte and reacts with a directed supply of oxygen (or air) to generate an electrical potential of 1.25-2 V. At the bottom, the depleted mercury is replenished with fresh sodium and reused. There is sophistication required in recycling the amalgam, but the reaction operates at room temperatures and requires no chemical feed stock beyond the sodium.

Whatever the reaction, the relatively low voltage produced appears to be stepped up to a more useful level using a double-wound variant of the induction coil invented in Paris by another German, Heinrich Ruhmkorff, around 1850. Whether this system is actually Captain Nemo's source of power or a ruse to avoid disclosure, six primary power cells are depicted at the forward end of the engine room with two induction coils mounted overhead. A similar, though scaled down, combination of Captain Nemo's sodium cell, and a Ruhmkorff coil also powers the portable undersea lights. The lamps themselves are likely Geissler tubes; glass tubes filled with CO_2 gas which gives off white light when subjected to a high voltage current. This precursor to modern fluorescent lights was invented in 1857.[75]

Captain Nemo replenishes his sodium supply by distilling seawater and separating out its mineral components at a secret refueling base. Probably this is done by the carbon reduction (using a blast furnace) of sodium carbonate (Na_2CO_3), which was the standard method of manufacture in the 1870s. However, the conversion of NaCl into Na_2CO_3 requires the rather complex Solvay process that involves the burning ("calcination") of limestone at ~1,000°C, an ammonia catalyst, and passing the brine (sea water) through two reaction towers.[76] Alternatively, it's possible, given Captain Nemo's expertise as an electro-chemist, that he has pioneered a Down's Cell. This device, patented in 1924, produces sodium through electrolysis by applying a low voltage to a molten mixture of NaCl and $CaCl_2$, heated above 500°C. Whichever the process, the ultimate source of energy is derived by burning sea coal, which Captain Nemo's crew mine from beneath the sea.

ENDURANCE AND PERFORMANCE

The impressive speeds attained and distances covered by Verne's *Nautilus* have caused its power source to be often referred to as "unlimited," but in fact refueling is shown to be required. Consider that Captain Nemo has been at sea for, at most, three years when he stops at his secret base inside the volcano to take on raw materials for his power generator. Although it is possible he is merely "topping off," his urgency, evidenced by his decision to draw from his stocks rather than conduct mining and processing operations, suggests this is a necessary refueling. As such, it provides a strong indication as to the upper limit on his operating endurance. Furthermore, as it is implied that this is not the first such refueling, we can infer that his actual refu-

eling interval is something less than 1.5 years. During the time Professor Aronnax is on board, the *Nautilus* covers approximately 10,000 leagues from November 7, 1867 to February 20, 1896 without refueling, which gives a lower limit on operating range. (Note: the definition of a league varies considerably; however, in Verne's use it equates to 2.16 nautical miles.) Further deductions can be made by examining the record of *Nautilus* sightings prior to November 1867, and the subsequent voyage provided in table 3.

There is a curious inconsistency in the reports of *Nautilus* sightings. On July 20, 1866 she is "five miles off the east coast of Australia" (p. 4) presumably headed eastward at about 21 kts, since three days later she is sighted in another location, "separated by a distance of more than 700 leagues" (p. 4). Verne then provides the next sighting as, "Fifteen days later, two thousand leagues further off," (p. 4) however, the position given (42° 15'N 60° 35'W) lies in the North Atlantic southeast of Nova Scotia; a sailing distance on the order of 5,200 leagues. Even if the distance described by Verne was intended as a direct measurement between two points on the globe, that actual distance would exceed the 2,000 league figure given by more than 50%. If we assume a typographical error so that the latitude is south vice north, then the resulting position east of Argentina would correlate with the 2,000 league distance given. However, the text goes on to describe the encounter, "in that portion of the Atlantic lying between the United States and Europe," (p. 4) supporting the northern Atlantic position, however improbable. Taken at face value, this fifteen-day run requires an average speed of at least 32 kts, and thus represents the fastest sustained performance by the Nautilus in the book. Such hyperbole was likely intentional on Verne's part to both astonish the readers and confound the characters in the book.

There are two notable gaps in the Nautilus sightings, from August 7, 1866 to March 5, 1867, and again from May 10, 1867 to November 5, 1868. During the first period she was operating in the mid-Atlantic and could conveniently have conducted a refueling at the secret base near the Canary Islands. That would give a time between refueling of about a year and at least 20,000 leagues of travel. If we assume a second secret refueling location somewhere in the Pacific (perhaps Christmas Island), then the second long interval between sightings would have provided an opportunity to refuel again without a long transit to the Atlantic, in which case the endurance interval could be on the order of six months, and perhaps as short as 10,000 leagues. This analysis effectively brackets the Nautilus's endurance between six months to a year, covering 10,000–20,000 leagues of travel. While this is a long and unrealistic power capacity for a battery, diesel-electric, or fuel cell driven submarine, it is extremely modest by modern nuclear standards and very much in line with first generation nuclear submarines, as well as modern, highly-compact modular nuclear technologies.

Table 3: Reported Transits of the *Nautilus*

Date	Location	Distance / Time / Min Average Speed
July 20, 1866	"Five miles off the east Coast of Australia"	700 leagues / 3 days / ~21 kts
July 23, 1866	"700 Leagues in 3 days"	
August 7, 1866	"15 days later…2,000 leagues away" 42° 15'N 60° 35'W (SE of Nova Scotia)	2,000 leagues / 15 days / ~14 kts ~5,200 leagues / 15 days / ~32 kts
	Refueling break?	~2,700 leagues / 211 days / ~1 kts
March 5, 1867	27° 30'N 72° 15'W (W of Bahamas)	1,600 leagues / 40 days / ~3.6 kts
April 13, 1867	45° 37'N 15° 12'W (E of Bay of Biscay)	5,000 leagues / 28 days / ~18 kts
May 10, 1867	"Sighted in the North Pacific"	
	Refueling break?	1,700 leagues? / 180 days /0.4 kts
November 5, 1867 November 7, 1867	31° 15'N 136° 42'E (SE of Japan) Professor Aronnax taken aboard	10,000 leagues / 106 days / ~8.5 kts
February 20, 1868	Refueling near Cape Verde Islands	
February 1868	Through the Mediterranean "600 leagues in 24 hrs times 2"	600 leagues / 48 hrs / ~27 kts
February 23–March 12, 1868	"100 leagues every 24 hours"	1,900 leagues / 19 days / ~9 kts
June 2–20, 1868	"20 days at 25 mph" ending in the maelstrom off the Lofoten Islands, Norway	~4,600 leagues / 20 days / 21 kts

The first nuclear submarine, USS *Nautilus*, exhibited an endurance and range remarkably similar to Captain Nemo's craft. She was refueled in 1957 after two years of operation in which she steamed 62,562 nm or 28,963 of Verne's leagues. USS *Nautilus* operated a 10 MW reactor providing 13,400 shp to propel her at speeds of up to 23 kts.[77] That speed was improved upon by USS *Albacore* with her unique tapered hull shape and 7,500 shp electric motor that could achieve burst speeds of 27 kts powered by her lead-acid batteries. Later, with the addition of a contra-rotating propeller driven by a second electric motor and a conversion to silver-zinc batteries, she attained 35 kts.[78]

This is an uncanny coincidence to the maximum speed of 34 kts observed by Professor Aronnax while on board the *Nautilus*. The similarities in dimension, displacement, and form between Verne's *Nautilus* and USS *Albacore* suggest that similar power and propulsive machinery would be required. This is further correlated by the figures for USS *Skipjack* which, although slightly larger (77 m in length, 9.63 m in beam giving 3,500 t displacement submerged), was the first submarine to merge the *Albacore* hull shape with nuclear power, possessing a 10 MW reactor that produced 15,000 shp, speed in excess of 31 kts, and giving the ship multi-year endurance.[79]

NUCLEAR IMAGINEERING

The disparity between the power needed by the *Nautilus*, and the battery technology alluded to by Captain Nemo, invites the speculation that he is obfuscating his true power supply, and that it is a nuclear source. It is a substantial leap to make from the text, but tantalizing historic connections make it irresistible to imagine. Consider that uranium was discovered as early as 1789, and the pure metal was first isolated by Eugène-Melchior Péligot working in Paris in 1841[80] during the time that Captain Nemo, as Prince Dakkar, was studying in Europe — likely in the same city. In that time, uranium was mined in Germany; however, it has been demonstrated that it can be extracted from seawater where the uranium concentration is approximately 3.3 mg per cubic meter of seawater. While this is too low to be economically viable even today, it certainly would appeal to Captain Nemo's obsession with sourcing his needs from the sea. Although the public discovery of uranium's radioactivity was not made until 1892 by Henri Becquerel, it is not too far-fetched that Prince Dakkar, undoubtedly a premier electro-chemist, could have made the same discovery years earlier while experimenting with alternative materials for battery cells. As demonstrated by Enrico Fermi in 1942, a critical nuclear reactor can be made by the ordered arrangement of natural uranium and graphite blocks to moderate the neutrons. In the case of

Chicago Pile-1, it took the form of a flattened ellipsoid, measuring 25 feet wide and 20 feet high, composed of 771,000 pounds of graphite, 80,590 pounds of uranium oxide, and 12,400 pounds of uranium metal when it went critical.[81] The materials and technology to do this were available to Prince Dakkar in the mid-1800s. Notably, what was lacking was the atomic theory; fundamental understanding of the structure of the atom and the discovery of the neutron, which did not occur until 1932. Could Dakkar have stumbled upon a self-sustaining fission reactor through trial and error experimentation involving heaps of uranium and graphite nearly a hundred years earlier? Physically the answer is yes, but without the insight into atomic theory there would seem to be little compulsion to do so. Perhaps in seeking an explanation of the *Nautilus*'s power source we arrogantly bind ourselves within the context of currently known science and thus preclude our consideration of the other alternative. The mid-19th century was the golden era for electrochemistry during which batteries, fuel-cells and other electro-chemical contrivances were invented and rapidly advancing, until eclipsed by the excitement of the atomic age that dawned with the new century. Prince Dakkar, studying in Europe at the forefront of the field, may well have made and kept secret a discovery that is as-yet unknown to modern science.

Submarine Development

John P. Holland, an Irish schoolteacher and self-taught engineer, began designing submarines shortly after emigrating to the United States in 1873. He built and operated several submarines before selling to the U.S. Navy in 1900 the vessel that would become its first commissioned submarine, USS Holland.

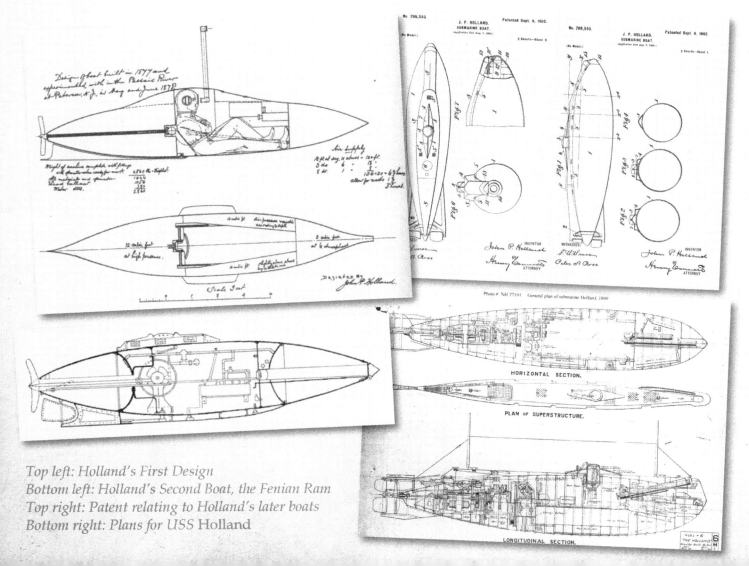

Top left: Holland's First Design
Bottom left: Holland's Second Boat, the Fenian Ram
Top right: Patent relating to Holland's later boats
Bottom right: Plans for USS Holland

Construction

INSPIRATIONS & COMPARISONS

Brutus de Villeroi was a French engineer who, in 1861, signed a contract for the first submarine to be built for the U.S. Navy. The 46-foot long *Alligator* was also the first to have a diver's lock-out chamber, on-board air compressors for air renewal and diver support, as well as an air-purifying system, and electrically detonated limpet mines. Towed from Philadelphia for operations in the James River, the boat proved to be too large to hide and support divers in the relatively shallow water. In 1863, it foundered and sank in a storm while being towed to an operating area off South Carolina. Interestingly, as early as 1832, de Villeroi had demonstrated a submersible in Nantes, France, and was reputedly a professor at the Saint-Donatien Junior Seminary in 1842, when Jules Verne enrolled as a student. As beguiling as it is to imagine that he may have provided some early inspiration, a solid link has never been established, and it is clear that the 1867 Exposition Universelle in Paris was the most direct influence on the conceptual design and technology described in the *Nautilus*.[82]

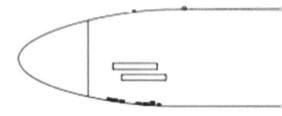

USS *Los Angeles*
SSN 688 (1976)

USS *Nautilus*
SSN 571 (1954)

The *H.L. Hunley*, a craft constructed of riveted wrought-iron plates, was the first submarine to sink a warship, employing a spar with attached torpedo.[83] *Plongeur*, the largest submarine of the 19th century, undoubtedly influenced Verne, and several elements of her design are reflected in the *Nautilus* including an integrated lifeboat. She was also the first submarine to utilize compressed air for emptying the ballast tanks; her size dictated by the need to accommodate large bottles of air, compressed to 12.25 atmospheres. Due to her flatness and length she suffered from longitudinal instability, and although equipped with a trim ballast system, it worked too slowly to be effective.[84] In size, shape, and displacement, the *Nautilus* is similar to USS *Albacore*, or the German Type 212 submarines, which have a crew of twenty-seven. The endurance and high speed performance of the *Nautilus* can only be achieved by modern nuclear submarines like the USS *Los Angeles*, which officially can reach speeds in excess of 25 knots or 29 mph; however, her extraordinary depth capability has yet to be matched except by small, purpose-built, deep-diving submersibles.

Figure 26: An illustration of the submarine Alligator[85] *that appeared in 1871 (left), and an early woodcut illustration of the* Nautilus *(right)*

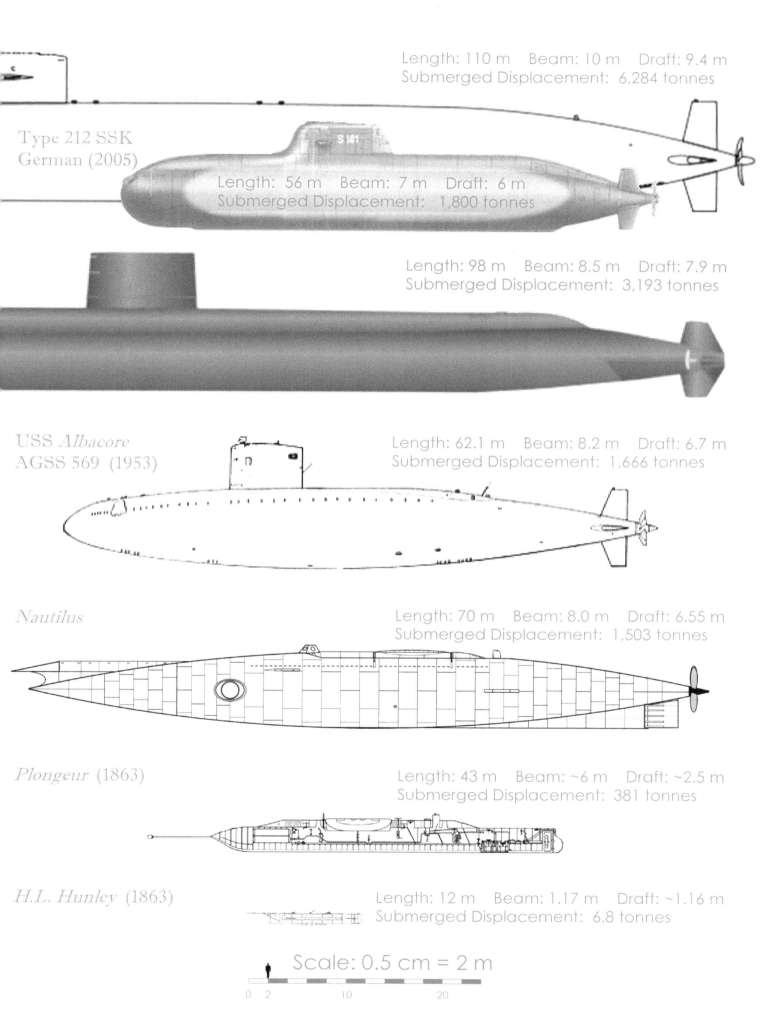

Length: 110 m   Beam: 10 m   Draft: 9.4 m
Submerged Displacement: 6,284 tonnes

Type 212 SSK
German (2005)

Length: 56 m   Beam: 7 m   Draft: 6 m
Submerged Displacement: 1,800 tonnes

Length: 98 m   Beam: 8.5 m   Draft: 7.9 m
Submerged Displacement: 3,193 tonnes

USS *Albacore*
AGSS 569 (1953)

Length: 62.1 m   Beam: 8.2 m   Draft: 6.7 m
Submerged Displacement: 1,666 tonnes

Nautilus

Length: 70 m   Beam: 8.0 m   Draft: 6.55 m
Submerged Displacement: 1,503 tonnes

Plongeur (1863)

Length: 43 m   Beam: ~6 m   Draft: ~2.5 m
Submerged Displacement: 381 tonnes

H.L. Hunley (1863)

Length: 12 m   Beam: 1.17 m   Draft: ~1.16 m
Submerged Displacement: 6.8 tonnes

Scale: 0.5 cm = 2 m

0 2   10   20

CURIOUS COINCIDENCE

In penning the memoir of Professor Aronnax, one is left to wonder what may have influenced Verne's characterization of Captain Nemo?

Late in 1868, the illustrators proposed modeling his appearance on that of Colonel Jean-Baptiste Charras. It was a choice that met with enthusiastic approval by Verne, suggesting that from that point forward, Verne may have linked the two in his mind.[86] After all, the republican colonel had played a leading role in the 1848 revolution in France, which sparked subsequent movements for political and social change throughout Europe. Then, as a member of the National Assembly, he opposed the coup that proclaimed Louis Napoleon emperor, and as a result, was forced to spend the remainder of his life in exile. These motivations and sympathies find parallels in the portrayal of Captain Nemo.

Understandably, many have come to regard Professor Aronnax's story as fiction, especially when it came to light that in the summer of 1865, Verne had received encouragement from fellow writer George Sand, to craft a tale that would, "…take us to the depths of the sea and that you will have your characters navigate in diving vessels that your science and your imag-

Figure 27: Captain Nemo and Colonel Jean-Baptiste Charras

ination will manage to improve."[87] But in what must surely be the most curious of coincidences, an amazing, yet obscure Catalan was launching a submarine at that very moment, whose sophistication would not be seen again for decades to come. Even more incredibly, the real life story of Narciso Monturiol i Estarriol is an uncanny parallel to the back story of Captain Nemo ultimately provided by Verne in *The Mysterious Island* (see table 4).

Beyond these chronological parallels lies the fascinating comparison of their motivations. On the surface

Table 4. Monturiol and Nemo Comparison[88]

Narciso Monturiol i Estarriol born 1819	Prince Dakkar born 1819
In 1830, Monturiol at age 11 is sent to Lieida to attend University of Cervera to study medicine	In 1829, Dakkar at age 10 is sent to Paris to attend Ecole Polytechnique to study engineering
Barcelona riots of 1835—Monturiol (16) quits medicine for law, moves to Barcelona and gets swept up in revolutionary fervor	Paris uprising of 1832—Dakkar (13) is swept up in the revolutionary fervor
Returning to Barcelona from his first exile, Monturiol marries in 1846 at age 27	Following the revolutions of 1848 in Paris, Dakkar ends his educational "exile" and returns to India, marrying in 1849 at age 30
Revolution finally arrives in Barcelona in 1854, Monturiol (35) is a leading figure	Sepoy Rebellion summer 1857, Dakkar (38) emerges as a leading figure
The revolution is crushed by 1856—in exile, with his fellow revolutionaries/utopians dead, Monturiol first expresses his submarine vision, which quickly becomes an obsession	Delhi falls in 1857, and Bahadur Shah Zafar is captured and exiled. Dakkar is forced to flee his homeland. The Battle of Gwalior in 1858 effectively ends the revolution.
Organization formed to build *Ictineo I* in October 1857	In hiding abroad, Dakkar begins designing the *Nautilus* in spring 1859
Ictineo I launched in June 1859 *Ictineo II* launched in October 1864	The *Nautilus* launched in 1865
Final demonstration of the chemical steam engine 1867 before bankruptcy forces *Ictineo* to be sold for scrap in 1868	Maelstrom engulfs Captain Nemo and the *Nautilus* in 1868

there would seem to be few similarities in character: "Captain Nemo, an enigmatic creature of Hugoesque will and Byronic terribilità who bears his inward wound through the depths of the sea, is not very like the mild Catalan.... Nemo was immeasurably rich, Monturiol hopelessly poor; Nemo bent on vengeance, Monturiol on world brotherhood." But as historian Robert Hughes goes on to note, fundamentally, they are both Utopians.[89] Until it was either overshadowed or consumed by modern communism, utopian philosophy flourished among intellectual liberals as an alternative to industrial society's inequalities and government oppression. Utopians of the first half of the 19th century were avid fans of science and technology, believing technical progress and social progress went everywhere together. Throughout his life, Monturiol was a liberal, a utopian, a revolutionary, and even an early communist. But once seized by the vision of a submarine boat, he subordinated those philosophical ideals and his anti-social activities to the notion that all such ambitions could be made reality by the promise of a true submarine. His biography[90] reveals the very Nemo-like motivations that drove Monturiol.

"He was on a mission to save the human race.... He further imagined that the submarine would open up all sorts of opportunities for the land-locked working classes—perhaps deep-sea fishing, salvage, operations, underwater farming, who knows? Above all, the submarine was for him, a tool of science. He longed to see what lay hidden beneath the blanket of ignorance that covered three-quarters of the earth's surface. He had only a vague idea of just what he might see down there, but he was sure that whatever it was would be of profound importance." (pp. 8–9)

"The quest for answers amounted to more than idle curiosity. Revealing the mysteries of the deep, for Monturiol, was really about the liberation of humankind....Like many of the prominent thinkers of his time he believed in Progress...the idea that the accumulation of scientific knowledge and the advance of social justice were one and the same thing. Strange as it may sound to our ears, his submarine project was a continuation of revolutionary politics by underwater means." (p. 9)

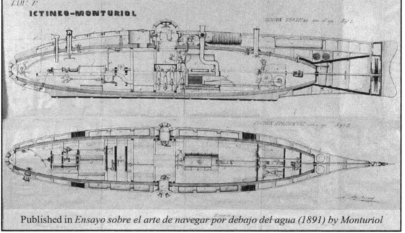

Published in *Ensayo sobre el arte de navegar por debajo del agua (1891)* by Monturiol

Figure 28: Narciso Monturiol (left), Monturiol's plans for the Ictineo II *(top), and a modern replica on display in Barcelona (bottom)*[91]

Ictineo's Accomplishments

Much like the Wright brothers, Monturiol derived his fundamental conceptual approach from studying nature, and then tackled each of the key challenges he identified with a controlled experimentation program. Thousands of careful experiments followed by a meticulous progression of testing led to an astonishing accomplishment of submarine firsts incorporated into his *Ictineo*:

- Double hull with the outer optimized for hydrodynamic form, the inner hull designed to resist pressure, and the space between used for ballast tanks
- Buoyancy calculations accommodated hull compression with depth
- Separate main ballast tanks for attaining near neutral buoyancy, and additional trim tanks for fine buoyancy control capable of being blown dry at depth with compressed air
- Detachable, redundant, lead drop-weights to provide emergency buoyancy
- Variable internal center-of-gravity weight for longitudinal trimming
- A calcium hydroxide based CO_2 scrubbing system
- An oxygen generation system using potassium chlorate and a manganese dioxide catalyst to execute the reaction without requiring additional heat
- An oxygen-hydrogen powered external lamp for underwater illumination
- Instrumentation for making accurate measurements of cabin O_2 and CO_2
- Glass viewports in the shape of a truncated cone
- Precision depth gauge and speedometer
- External manipulator arm
- An air-independent, chemically powered steam engine that exhausted oxygen for the life support system
- Cannon capable of being reloaded and fired from a submerged position

Unlike Bushnell's *Turtle*, Fulton's *Nautilus*, or Bauer's *Brandtaucher*, which preceded him, Monturiol's submarine advances were repeatedly demonstrated during hundreds of hours spent underwater from 1865 to 1867. Some dives lasted as long as 8 hours and reached 30 meters—self imposed limits since *Ictineo* was capable of much more.

Pencil drawing of *Ictineo's* launch

When Monturiol writes, "The submarine would liberate mankind from the fetters of the earth's atmosphere…" (p. 103) it is as if Captain Nemo himself is speaking. In the end, however, "the real argument Monturiol made for the submarine's utility was really just a statement of hope." (p. 106) Regardless of his tenuous justification, his vision was without precedent, its technical ambition exceeding even Verne's conception of the *Nautilus* (see detail at left).

> "He envisioned a craft capable of descending to any depth, even to the very bottom of the ocean; capable of moving around underwater at will; capable of sustaining human life indefinitely in the inhospitable environment of the deep; and enabling humankind to interact with the watery environment in all the many ways—seeing, hearing, grabbing—available on the surface. What he intended to build was, in a certain sense, the world's first true submarine." (p. 10)

There is no evidence to suggest that Verne was aware of Monturiol and his submarine accomplishments, which received little notoriety within Spain and virtually none beyond. However, Monturiol, who was fluent in French, did make a visit to Paris in 1862, and then attended the World Exposition in London where the English journal *Twice a Week* published a favorable review of his project, creating an opportunity that tantalizes with possibility. Yet it seems likely that had Verne been aware of the *Ictineo,* and especially its innovative life support mechanisms, he would have included this technological capability in his vision for the *Nautilus* rather than suffer the daily surface ventilation requirement related by Professor Aronnax. For those who maintain the Professor's story is a fanciful fabrication, this is cited as further evidence of a cunning author depriving the *Nautilus* of a key technology so as to be able to craft the suspense of becoming trapped within the ice and slowly suffering the increasingly stagnant air. The credibility of Professor Aronnax's memoir is further undermined by the fact that 1862 is when Verne wrote the first of his signature works of fiction, *Five Weeks in a Balloon,* and met the publisher Pierre-Jules Hetzel with whom he would collaborate so spectacularly on all his successive literary adventures.

WHERE WAS THE NAUTILUS BUILT?

"'Professor, I set up my workshops on a desert isle in the middle of the ocean. There my workmen—that is to say my gallant comrades whom I have trained and educated—and myself put together the Nautilus. When our work was finished, we burned all evidence of our stay on the isle. I would have blown it up if that had been possible.'" p. 89

Although Verne provides clues to Captain Nemo's identity and background throughout the narrative, his history is only fully revealed in a subsequent work entitled *The Mysterious Island.* It relates how, in 1858, Prince Dakkar, later to become Captain Nemo, escapes India after suffering defeat and the execution of his family at the hands of the British, and disappears with approximately twenty associates. Where did he go?

As the Indian rebellion of 1857 spread, Sepoy regiments, seeking a figure that could unite all Indians, Hindu and Muslim alike, accepted Bahadur Shah Zafar as the Emperor of India. He was to be the last Mughal emperor. In suppressing the rebellion, the British executed his sons and grandson and then tried and exiled him to British controlled Rangoon (now Yangon). His departure as Emperor marked the end of more than three centuries of Mughal rule in India and the inception of the British Raj. Bahadur Shah died in exile on 7 November 1862.[92] Would Captain Nemo have sought refuge somewhere in Southeast Asia to remain near his former Emperor? Possibly, though for a notorious fugitive of his stature, avoiding the attention of the British during this period of history would have been difficult. Much of the region was under British rule, though notable exceptions included the Dutch East Indies (Indonesia), Vietnam (being colonized by the French), the Philippines (under Spanish rule), and Siam (Thailand), which was maintaining a precarious independence between competing imperial powers.

The voyage with Professor Aronnax occurs in 1867 who concludes, based on the publication dates of books in the library, that Captain Nemo has been at sea for "not more than three years." That provides a seven year period from 1858 to 1865 in which the *Nautilus* was constructed. But where was the work done? In a rather offhand remark, Captain Nemo refers to an island in the middle of the ocean. Certainly the vast oceans from India to the Pacific contain no shortage of uninhabited specks of land matching that description. However, the realities of constructing a submarine as large and advanced as the *Nautilus* quickly narrow down the scope of suitable candidates. All of the major components must be fabricated by the heavy industry of Europe, and at one point Captain Nemo rattles off many of his vendors. All of these parts, which include a substantial quantity of large steel pieces, would have to have been shipped to a seaport of significant size in order to escape notice. Frequent trips to ferry these incoming components, as well as the supplies necessary to maintain his workforce on an austere island, would argue for a secret assembly location within a short sail of this major seaport. This fact alone eliminates most of the remote expanses of the Pacific Ocean. Major seaports in Southeast Asia in the mid-19th century include: Adelaide, Melbourne, Bombay, Calcutta, Rangoon (Yangon), Hong Kong, Singapore, Manila, Batavia (Jakarta), and Sourabaya. Unfortunately for Captain Nemo, many of these were under British control.

- Singapore grew in importance as a coaling station from the 1840s onward. It became the administrative capital of British Malaya and developed into an important processing center for crude oil, rubber, and tin.[93]

- Rangoon, along with all of Lower Burma, was seized by the British in the Second Anglo-Burmese War of 1852, and subsequently transformed into the commercial and political hub of British Burma.[94]

- Hong Kong Island was occupied by the British in 1841 during The First Opium War (1839–1842), and was subsequently ceded to Britain in 1842 under the Treaty of Nanking, when the territory became a Crown colony. British traders, opium dealers, and merchants rapidly developed the city, and in 1860 Britain was granted a rent-free perpetual lease on the Kowloon Peninsula under the Convention of

Beijing, which formally ended hostilities in the Second Opium War (1856–1858).[95]

- In Australia, a gold rush began in the early 1850s, and although from 1855-1890 the six colonies individually gained responsible government, managing most of their own affairs, they remained part of the British Empire with the Colonial Office in London retaining control of some matters, notably foreign affairs, defense, and international shipping.[96]

- New Zealand was administered as a part of the Australian colony of New South Wales until becoming a British colony in its own right in 1841. The discovery of gold in 1861 caused a worldwide rush that in three years more than doubled the population to 164,000.[97]

A non-British port would have definitely been preferable, and Captain Nemo must have certainly been dismayed and angered at the spread of imperialism throughout the region and growing strength of the British empire. There existed few options in the region that lay outside British control.

- Saigon was seized in 1859 by a French naval expedition who subsequently occupied three adjoining provinces in 1869, thus completing the territory of the colony they would call Cochin-China. Although Captain Nemo seems somewhat sympathetic to the French, this volatility and the undeveloped nature of Saigon as an industrial port would have rendered it unsuitable for his purpose.[98]

- Thailand remained free of imperialist influences, but only because her leaders skillfully parlayed opposing French and British interests into a position of neutrality. Captain Nemo would have likely viewed this tenuous position as too vulnerable to provide adequate haven for his activities, and Thailand's ports at the time were insufficiently developed to provide the necessary cover for large steel and machinery shipments.[99]

- Batavia (Jakarta) was a well-established trading center by the mid-1850s and a longtime Dutch colony. Batavia's long struggle with malaria throughout the 18th century had kept the city from growing to its potential, but by 1860 it was known as the "Queen of the East" and on the cusp of a strong expansion that would eventually require the construction of a new harbor in 1877. Railway construction, which began in 1864, suggests that heavy industry shipments were occurring by then, and infrastructure could be found that would have been essential to receiving and organizing material for the *Nautilus*.[100]

- Spanish Manila was seen in the 19th century as a model of colonial governance that effectively put the interests of the original inhabitants of the islands before those of the colonial power. Spain invested heavily in education and infrastructure, and a great deal of construction projects were undertaken during this period that put the Philippine economy and standard of living ahead of most of its Asian neighbors and even many European countries at that time. Among them was a railway system for Luzon, a tramcar network for Manila, and the Puente Colgante (now known as the Quezon Bridge), Asia's first steel suspension bridge. This favorable political and economic climate would have attracted Captain Nemo's attention, and the ongoing construction boom would have ensured that steel and machinery shipments destined for the *Nautilus* would have hardly been noticed. A curious facet of the nearby town of Cainta may have held additional attraction for Captain Nemo. During the brief British occupation of Luzon (1762–1763), part of its British India

Figure 29: 19th-century Manila[101]

troops known as Sepoys lived and intermarried with the natives in one of the town's barrios. They left an indelible impression on the culture and features of Cainta residents that persists even today.[102]

Batavia and Manila emerge as the most plausible candidates in all of Southeast Asia to serve as a staging port for the *Nautilus's* construction materials. As a practical matter, the desert island where the submarine was to be assembled would need to be located within a short sailing distance of the port, yet far enough away to escape attention of the shipping traffic. A location some distance from any mainland would also be preferable to reduce the likelihood of casual visits from local fishermen. Both Batavia and Manila have islands that meet these requirements nicely.

Christmas Island, located only 350 sailing miles southwest from Batavia, was isolated and uninhabited until 1888. Surrounded by deep water, it has only one tenuous anchorage, which would complicate material deliveries, and the steep cliffs of the shoreline offer few places conducive to shipbuilding. But these same features would also deter unwelcome visitors. The island has extensive deposits of calcium carbonate and calcium phosphate; two potentially useful resources for the chemistry that powers the *Nautilus*. One consequence of the limestone geology is that the island is riddled with caves, some of large dimension located underwater. With its irregular geography capped by a 1,184 ft mountain and covered by tropical rainforest, it is the closest analog of the Lincoln Island described as the *Nautilus's* final resting place in *The Mysterious Island*. The fact that Christmas Island is the nearest land to the location given for Captain Nemo's underwater coral cemetery, makes the island of even greater interest.[103]

The Paracel Islands, located about a three-day sail west of the Philippines, is an uninhabited archipelago of some thirty islets, sandbanks and reefs, sufficiently treacherous that most shipping steers clear. Any of these would have been adequate for Captain Nemo's purposes, however, there is one island that lies separate from the two main groups, and its name makes it especially compelling as the site of the *Nautilus's* construction...Lincoln Island. According to the account given in *The Mysterious Island*, Lincoln Island is supposedly located about 2,500 km (1,600 mi) east of New Zealand

at 34°57□S, 150°30□W. In reality, the closest island to those coordinates is Rapa Iti, located some 600 mi northeast at 27°36□S, 144°22□W. Although there is no suggestion that this final resting place of the *Nautilus* is also the island of its construction, this coincidence of name and its suitableness for construction makes the real Lincoln Island (16°40'N, 112°44'E) an irresistible choice as the site where the *Nautilus* was built.

The island's name is likely derived from its traditional Vietnamese name "linh-con," which can be translated approximately as "spirited child"; a serendipitously apt moniker for Captain Nemo's construction refuge. The island is covered with brush and fairly high trees, including coconut palm trees, and surrounded by a coral reef. Water depths increase sharply on the northern and eastern sides of the island but the southern and southwestern regions are shallow. Although there is little fresh water, a well was discovered into which fresh water filters, and the abundant rainfall could be collected to provide an adequate supply for a small working crew. Among the Paracels, history has recorded such minor activities as the Chinese construction of a temple and the planting of trees on other islands in the archipelago in the 1830s, but there is no record of any visits to Lincoln Island other than a brief survey conducted in 1883 by a German government expedition. It is also interesting to note that adjacent to a clearing near the beach on the western side of the island, a channel has been cut through the reef at some point much prior to recent Chinese development. This would be essential to land supplies ashore or to launch a vessel to sea, and would be a logical vestige of any shipbuilding activity. Photographs on page 95 depict this geographical feature of Lincoln Island, and we propose that this is the beach where the *Nautilus* was born.[104]

Figure 30: Batavia circa 1865

South China Sea

North
Reef

West Sand

Tree Island
North Island

AMPHITRITE
GROUP

Rocky Island
Woody Island

Dido
Bank

Iltis
Bank

CRESCENT
GROUP

Observation
Bank

Lincoln
Island

Pyramid
Rock

Pattle Island
Robert Island

NEPTUNA
BANKS

Money Island

Drummond Island
Duncan Island

Antelope
Reef

Vuladdore
Reef

JEHANGIRE
REEFS

Discovery
Reef

Bremen
Bank

Bombay
Reef

Passu Keah

Paracel
Archipelago

XXVI.

RYUKYU JA

Tropic of Canc

Taipei

Kao-hsiung

Taiwan

Manda

Hong Kong S.A.R.

Macau
S.A.R.

BURMA

Hanoi

Zhanjiang

kyab

LAOS

Haiphong

Pratas
Island

Luzon
Strait

BABUYAN ISLANDS

Ph

Chiang
Mai

Vientiane

Vinh

Gulf of
Tonkin

Hainan
Dao

Luzon

Rangoon

CHAÎNE ANNAMITIQUE

thein

Hue

Da Nang

PARACEL
ISLANDS

THAILAND

Nakhon
Ratchasima

VIETNAM

Manila

Mawlamyine

Dawei

Bangkok

CAMBODIA

Nha
Trang

South

Mindoro

Samar

ANDAMAN
ISLANDS
(INDIA)

Phnom Penh

Ho Chi Minh
City

China

Sea

P H I L I P P I N E S

Panay

Iloilo

Andaman

Long
Xuyen

Cebu

Sea

Gulf of
Thailand

SPRATLY
ISLANDS

Palawan

Bacolod

Negros

Cagayan de Oro

NICOBAR
ISLANDS
(INDIA)

Phuket

Songkhla

Sulu Sea

Mindanao

Zamboanga

Davao

at channel

George Town

Ipoh

Bandar Seri
Begawan

Kota Kinabalu

a Aceh

MALAYSIA

BRUNEI

Celebes

Medan

Kuala Lumpur

KEPULAUAN
NATUNA

Sea

u Simeulue

Melaka

MALAYSIA

Manado

Pulau Nias

Singapore
SINGAPORE

Kuching

Borneo

Moluc

Padang

Pulau
Bangka

Pontianak

Samarinda

Palu

Sea

Pulau Siberut

Selat
Karimata

Sulawesi
(Celebes)

Ceram

KEPULAUAN
MENTAWAI

Sumatra

Palembang

Banjarmasin

Kendari

Buru

Ambo

Tanjungkarang-
Telukbetung

Billiton

Java Sea

Makassar

Jakarta

Semarang

Madura

Flores Sea

I N D O N E S I A

Banda Se

Bandung

Java

Surabaya

Bali

Lombok

Flores

Dili

Selat Sunda

Denpasar

Sumbawa

Sumba

Kupang

Timor

EAST TIMOR

Selat Lombok

Christmas Island
(AUSTRALIA)

Timor
Sea

Cocos
(Keeling)
Islands
(AUSTRALIA)

Ashmore and
Cartier Islands
(AUSTRALIA)

Indian Ocean

Prior to 2012

106

2018 Appearance

"Linh Con" Island !

16° 40' N   112° 44' E

Recent development by China is rapidly changing the appearance of Lincoln Island as well as others of the Paracel Archipelago. Satellite imagery shows a well-used dirt road now surrounds the island along the coast and crosses the interior. At four opposing points large tower structures have been built, and a marine navigation beacon has been installed on the southeast side of the island. This construction activity and the probability of continuous or frequently recurring human occupation has significantly altered any original footprint of Captain Nemo's shipyard activity. Thus we may have lost the chance to conclusively confirm this as the site of the *Nautilus*'s construction.

The other island of significance to the operation of the *Nautilus* is Captain Nemo's secret refueling base. It is described as a grotto six miles in circumference contained within a volcano that is 1,800 feet high and located somewhere in the Canary or Cape Verde Island chains. In reality, within these volcanically active archipelagos, the island of Lanzarote features a 1,998 foot high volcano named Monte Corona that created the world's longest known submarine lava tube about 4,000 years ago. This subterranean struc-

ture extends from the cone of the volcano for 6 km (3.7 mi) above sea level, and for another 1.5 km (0.93 mi) below the sea—a portion known as the Tunnel de la Atlantida. The interior of the tunnel reaches a height of some 50 m (164 ft) with widths that approach 15 m (49 ft).[107] There are peculiar rock formations and structures: lava channels, solid blocks dragged along by the current, large drops of lava, salt deposits, successive strata of solidified lava, etc. Although its existence has been known for hundreds of years, it was only in the 19th century that the cave was transformed into a place to visit for European tourists, scholars, and scientists traveling through the Canary Islands. Surely Verne was aware of the descriptions published by the geologist Georg Hartung in 1855 and the geologist and botanist Karl Von Fritsch in 1863 when he conceived of this refuge for the *Nautilus*.[108] In October 2011, a submarine eruption occurred about 2 km (1.25 mi) south of the island of El Hierro, further evidence of the continued volcanic activity in the area, and making the existence of Captain Nemo's as-yet undiscovered secret refueling cave a plausible notion indeed.

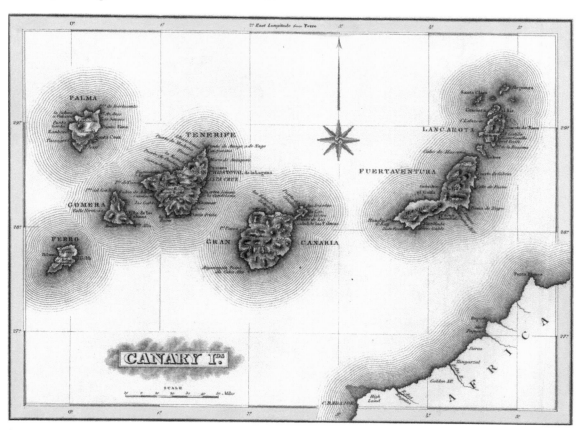

Figure 31: Mid-19th-century chart of the Canary Islands

HOW WAS THE NAUTILUS BUILT?

"'Each of these firms got my specifications under a different name.'" p. 89

Only the largest and most advanced industrial companies of Europe were capable at that time of providing the components to build the *Nautilus*. Captain Nemo makes no secret of some of the many vendors that he clandestinely approached, and they provide insight into the manufacturing capabilities and technology of the Victorian Age.

"'Its keel was forged by Creusot, in France...'" p. 89

In 1836, Joseph-Eugene Schneider and his brother Adolphe purchased a derelict ironworks in Burgundy, near the town of Le Creusot, and founded Schneider Brothers & Co. (later renamed Schneider & Co.). Two years later the company produced the first steam locomotive to be built in France. Eugene Schneider, along with the company's chief engineer, François Bourdon, developed the world's first true steam hammer at the Schneider works in 1841. Schneider and Co. went on to build 110 steam hammers of all sizes between 1843 and 1867, twenty-six of which were employed by the firm itself. As the jobs grew more demanding, the hammers grew correspondingly larger, and the Schneiders eventually saw a need for a hammer of colossal proportions. The Creusot steam hammer was completed in 1877, and with its ability to deliver a blow of up to 100 tons, eclipsed the previous record set by the German firm Krupp, whose steam hammer "Fritz" with its 50

ton blow had held the title as the world's most powerful steam hammer since 1861. In celebration of this technological achievement, a full scale wooden replica of the Creusot hammer was built and displayed at the Paris Universal Exposition of 1878.[110]

"'...the propeller shaft by Pen & Co. in London...'" p. 89

Penydarren Ironworks was the fourth of the great ironworks established at Merthyr Tydfil in South Wales. It was built in 1784 by the brothers Samuel, Jeremiah, and Thomas Homfray. Because the owners of the Cyfarthfa Ironworks dominated the management of Glamorganshire Canal, the other Merthyr Tydfil ironworks built a tramroad to Abercynon, bypassing the upper sections of the canal. This "Penydarren Tramroad" was used for a trial of the first railway steam locomotive, built by Richard Trevithick. In 1802, Trevithick had built one of his high-pressure steam engines to drive a hammer at the Penydarren Ironworks, and under the supervision of Samuel Homfray, he mounted the engine on wheels and turned it into a locomotive. Despite many people's doubts, it was shown that, provided the gradient was sufficiently gentle, it was possible to successfully haul heavy carriages along a "smooth" iron road using the adhesive weight alone of a suitably heavy and powerful steam locomotive. Trevithick's was probably the first to do so; however, some of the short cast iron plates of the tramroad broke under the locomotive, as they were intended only to support the lighter axle

Figure 32: Creusot steam hammer[109]

Figure 33: Penydarren Ironworks circa 1875[111]

load of horse-drawn wagons, and so the tramroad returned to horse power after the initial test run. Samuel Homfray left the business in 1813. In 1819, the partners were William Forman and William Thompson of London, who sold the works in 1859 to the Dowlais Iron Company. The works were used intermittently by various others until 1883. Some remains of the works can still be seen.[112]

"'...the sheet-iron plates for the hull by Laird's in Liverpool...'" p. 89

John Laird was a Scottish shipbuilder and one of the first to use iron in the construction of ships. He realized that the techniques of bending iron plates and riveting them together to build ships were similar to the principles involved in making boilers. Laird's first vessel was a 60 ft, 60 ton, pre-fabricated iron lighter, the *Wye*, built in 1829, which was used on canals and lakes in Ireland. In 1834, he built the paddle steamer *John Randolph* for Savannah, Georgia, stated to be the first iron ship seen in America. For the East India Company, he built in 1839 the *Nemesis*, the first iron vessel carrying guns. In 1839, Laird built their first screw-propelled steamer, *Robert F. Stockton*, a 63 ft tug for use on North American waterways. By 1840, Laird had built another twenty-one iron paddle-steamers, including four gun boats for anti-piracy patrols for the British East India Company. Further orders for paddle frigates included the 1,400 ton HMS *Birkenhead* (which he designed) of 1848, which was famously wrecked off South Africa with the

loss of over 400 soldiers in 1852. Perhaps their most famous vessel was the Confederate raider CSS *Alabama*. In 1857, the business moved to a new yard upstream from the Woodside Ferry, where it remained.

In October 1863, John Laird and his shipbuilding company were caught making two naval ram vessels for the Confederate States Navy: *El Toussoun* and *El Monastir*. The names of these two ships do not appear to hold any significance in the Confederacy, which leads to the possibility that this was a covert contract between Laird and the Confederate navy. British marines raided these ships during construction, forcing off the workmen and their equipment. The Royal Navy additionally deployed a gunship, HMS *Heron*, to the area to prevent the half constructed ships from leaving the port. Laird then sued the British government for impeding his construction. As a Member of Parliament at the time, Laird was certainly aware of the intricacies of international relations between the United Kingdom and the Northern and Southern states during the American Civil War, and his motivations for continuing work on this project are unknown. Perhaps it was this revolutionary sympathy that allowed Captain Nemo to overlook his British aversion and contract with Laird for his sheet-iron plates.[113]

"'...the propeller itself by Scott in Glasgow...'" p. 89

Scotts' Shipbuilding and Engineering Company Limited, often referred to simply as Scotts, was a Scot-

Figure 34: Motala Verkstad employees in the late 19th century[114]

Figure 35: Advertisement for Scotts[115]

tish shipbuilding company based in Greenock on the River Clyde. The Company was founded by John Scott who commenced shipbuilding at Greenock in 1711. The Scott family took over the Greenock Foundry in 1790, and C. G. Scott started building at Cartsdyke Dockyard in 1850 as Scott & Company. John Scott and Robert Scott acquired the adjacent yard of R. Steele & Company in 1883 to create the Cartsburn Dockyard, which was laid out for naval construction. Notable vessels built included the early Royal Mail Steam Packet Company liners *Clyde, Solway, Tweed* and *Dee* in 1841, SS *Thetis* of 1857, the early tanker *Narragansett* in 1903, and the submarine *S1* in 1914. An interesting footnote, Scotts' Assistant Manager James Richardson devised an early snorkel for submarines, for which they were granted a British patent, however it was not taken up by the Admiralty for use by the Royal Navy.[116]

"'...the tanks were manufactured by Cail & Co. in Paris...'" p. 89

The Derosne and Cail Company was a sizable iron and steel engineering firm in Paris in the latter half of the 19th century. They were one of several manufacturers of the Crampton-type locomotive that was built in various countries from 1846 to 1864, but was perhaps most popularly used in France. It was a steam-powered locomotive, particularly well suited for the transport of passengers because of its stability and its speed: a Crampton locomotive could haul twelve to sixteen carriages, totaling 100 to 130 tons, at a speed of 60 km/h, and when running on its own, it could reach 120 km/h.[117] A Crampton locomotive built by Cail & Co. was on display in the Galerie des Machines in Paris at the World's Fair in 1889. The Galerie in itself was another product of the company, and with a length of 2,200 m and a portal arch span of 114 m, was the largest single-span structure in the world at that time.[118]

"'...the engine by Krupp in Prussia...'" p. 89

Friedrich Krupp launched the family's metal-based activities, building a pioneering steel foundry in Essen in 1810. His son Alfred, known as "the Cannon King" or as "Alfred the Great," invested heavily in new technology to become a significant manufacturer of steel rollers (used to make eating utensils) and railway wheels. He also invested in fluidized hotbed technologies (notably the Bessemer process) and acquired many mines in Germany and France. The company began to make steel cannons in the 1840s — especially for the Russian, Turkish, and Prussian armies. At the Great Exhibition of 1851, he exhibited

Figure 36: Erection of the prefabricated truss girders for the Galerie des Machines constructed by Cail & Co. in Paris for the World's Fair in 1889[119]

Figure 37: Crampton locomotive of the kind built by Derosne and Cail Company[120]

a 6-pounder made entirely from cast steel, and a solid flawless ingot of steel weighing 4,300 pounds (2,000 kg), more than twice as much as any previously cast. He surpassed this with a 100,000-pound (45,000 kg) ingot for the Paris Exposition in 1855. Krupp's exhibits caused a sensation in the engineering world, and the Essen works became famous. In 1851, another successful innovation, no-weld railway wheels, began the company's primary revenue stream, from sales to railroads in the United States. Low non-military demand and government subsidies meant that the company specialized more and more in weapons: by the late 1880s the manufacture of armaments represented around 50% of Krupp's total output. When Alfred started with the firm, it had five employees. At his death, 20,000 people worked for Krupp—making it the world's largest industrial company and the largest private company in the German empire.[121]

"'…its ram by the Motala shops in Sweden…'" p. 89

Motala Verkstad was founded in 1822 by Baltzar von Platen to manufacture the large quantity of iron parts, tools, locks, and bridges that were needed during the construction of Göta Canal. During Otto Edvard Carlsund's leadership between 1843-1870, Motala Verkstad became internationally famous. The company received several awards and was praised at world exhibitions.[122] A Swedish company may seem an odd choice among the other industrial heavyweights, however it is worth noting that before the Bessemer process, steel was manufactured by a process of adding carbon to carbon-free wrought iron. The most dif-ficult and work-intensive part of the process was the production of wrought iron usually imported from the finery forges in Sweden.[123]

"'…the precision instruments by Hart Brothers in New York…'" p. 89

The specific company to which Captain Nemo refers would seem to have been lost to history, but in the mid-1800s, central New York was home to a rapidly expanding manufacturing industry and universities, such as Rensselaer Polytechnic Institute, that created fertile ground for many small precision instrument companies to flourish. One example is Taylor Instruments, founded in 1851 in Rochester, New York by George Taylor. The company started out making instruments for the professional market in a very small factory shop. During the Industrial Revolution, Taylor grew with the demands for new technologies, streamlining processes and advancing with the manufacturing world. In addition to thermometers and hygrometers, the company also made incubator thermometers and controlled-environment instruments, establishing itself in the professional market. Gurley Enterprise is another example, established by William and Lewis E. Gurley in 1845, brothers who were both alumni of Rensselaer Polytechnic Institute. In 1885 Gurley started making hydrologic equipment, and in the early 1900s acquired many new fields including paper testing equipment and thermometers. The W. & L. E. Gurley Building in Troy was named a National Historic Landmark in 1983, and in 1993 the company adopted its current name of Gurley Precision Instruments.[124]

WHAT DID THE NAUTILUS COST?

"'…an iron ship costs about 1,125 francs per metric ton. The Nautilus displaces 1,500 metric tons. It cost, therefore, 1,687,000 francs, or 2,000,000 francs with all its furnishing or 4,000,000 or 5,000,000 francs with the art works and other collections it contains.'" p. 89

To the modern reader, the figures Captain Nemo cites for the cost of the Nautilus are assumed to be impressive considered in their historical context, but gaining a true appreciation for their impact on a mid-19th century audience and assessing their realism compared to actual submarine construction costs turns out to be a complex endeavor. It is reasonable to assume that Captain Nemo's family wealth was maintained in rupees,

Table 5: Comparison cost of the *Nautilus* using three indicators[125]

		1865 The *Nautilus* 2 M francs ~$693,000	1900 USS *Holland* $236,615 (sold to U.S. Navy for $150,000)	1916 USS *Schley* class $500,000	1943 WWII Fleet Boat *Gato & Balao* class $3.3 M	2008 USS *Virginia* Class ~$2B Ger. U214 Class $330 M
Cost of sub in year produced						
Cost of the *Nautilus* inflated by	Consumer Price Index		$357,000	$467,000	$759,000	$9.45 M
	Production Wage		$848,000	$1.47 M	$6.06 M	$160 M
	Economy Cost		$1.44 M	$3.48 M	$13.9 M	$1.01 B

which traditionally were based on a silver standard. The discovery of more and more silver deposits from the 1860s onward drove many economies to the gold standard and resulted in tremendous devaluation for those, like India, that remained tied to silver. But Captain Nemo is likely to have been unaffected, having had to transfer his wealth to a more accessible currency (francs) in anticipation of financing the *Nautilus*. The majority of the components to construct the *Nautilus* would have been purchased between 1860 and 1865. During those years, the French national currency was the franc germinal, which contained 290.32 mg of fine gold. The coinage, colloquially known as "Napoleons," were originally minted in two denominations, 20 and 40 francs for Napoleon Bonaparte.[126] Although the portraits and legends changed with the political changes in France, the denomination remained in usage until the First World War. In 1865 France joined the Latin Monetary Union, standardizing their currency with Belgium, Italy, and Switzerland to a common ratio of 4.5 g of silver or 0.290322 g of gold (a ratio of 15.5 to 1). Bimetallism gave way to a pure gold standard in 1873, and the currency enjoyed relative stability until the outbreak of World War I. Comparison with current gold prices gives Captain Nemo's 2 million francs a modern value of about €20 million or US$24 million. While a considerable figure, this sum seems insufficient to inspire the awe registered by Professor Aronnax. In terms of purchasing power, a franc from this period (known as an "old franc") was the equivalent of €3.5 (2007), thus 2

million francs would equate to only €7 million or US$9 million based on the consumer price index (CPI).[127]

However, CPI may not be the best indicator, as it represents commodities confined to consumer goods and services, while the *Nautilus* clearly is not. Other measures of worth have been developed[128] that consider both the type of transaction or asset and the appropriate comparable, or indicator. As a large-scale, unique project, a better indicator than CPI might be economy cost, which measures the relative share of a (large government) project as a percent of the output of the economy. This measure indicates opportunity cost, or the importance of the project to society as a whole, in terms of total output of the economy, and uses the share of gross domestic product (GDP). Values provided by this indicator are useful for comparing the *Nautilus* to subsequent government-funded submarine acquisitions. But perhaps the best indicator for providing a visceral sense of how expensive the *Nautilus* would have seemed to period readers is provided by the labor cost comparison. Labor cost of a project is measured using the relative wage of the workers that might be used to build the project. For submarine construction, production worker wages are used instead of the unskilled wage. Comparisons of all three indicators against increasingly modern submarine acquisitions are provided in table 5. Against these actual acquisition costs for real submarines, the estimate for the *Nautilus* appears highly realistic.

HOW WAS THE NAUTILUS ASSEMBLED?

"'Each section, Professor, came to me from a different point on the globe and was sent to a cover address.'" p. 89

That Captain Nemo procured so many components for the *Nautilus* from British manufacturers may seem at odds with his animosity toward that nation, but in fact, he may have had few alternatives. In the 19th century the British shipbuilding industry was the largest in the world. During the thirty years between 1850 and 1880, British steamship tonnage increased by 1,600%. In the same period, the tonnage of steamships owned by the rest of the world grew by only 440%—and the majority of these would have come from British yards. By 1880 over half the world's steamships flew the British flag. Between 1892 and 1894, British yards pro-

duced more than four-fifths of the world's commercial tonnage.[130] A second and perhaps even more compelling reason to source much of the *Nautilus* from Britain was their dominance in steel production. In 1850 Sheffield produced some 35,000 tons of steel—more than half of world production.[131] Commercial production of steel using the Bessemer process, which improved quality and lowered cost, began in Sheffield in 1858. It is beguiling to imagine Captain Nemo facilitating this production development in order to meet his needs, but this seems unlikely since patents for the process were first filed in 1855.

Iron had been gradually adopted in ship construction, and although by 1850 ships were being built entirely of wrought iron, weed and barnacle fouling experienced by these ships kept composite construction (wood timbers over an iron frame) the dominant approach where speed was required. The SS *Great Eastern*, on which Verne traveled to the United States, represented the next great development in shipbuilding. Built in 1858, it used longitudinal stringers for strength, inner and outer hulls, and bulkheads to form multiple watertight compartments. After 1872, steel started to be introduced as a material for construction, providing greater structural strength for a lower weight. The French Navy led the way with the use of steel in its fleet, starting with the *Redoutable*, laid down in 1873 and launched in 1876. *Redoutable* nonetheless had wrought iron armor plate, and part of her exterior hull was iron rather than steel. Even though Britain led the world in steel production, the Royal Navy was slow to adopt steel warships. The Bessemer process for steel manufacture produced too many imperfections for large-scale use on ships. Beginning in 1865, French manufacturers used the Siemens-Martin process to produce adequate steel, but British naval technology lagged behind. The first all-steel warships built by the Royal Navy were the dispatch vessels *Iris* and *Mercury*, laid down in 1875 and 1876.[132]

Figure 38: USS Nautilus *(V-6 / SS-168) under construction at Portsmouth Naval Shipyard in 1927*[129]

After fleeing India in 1857, it seems reasonable to assume that it may have taken Captain Nemo a couple of years to identify a suitable clandestine construction location for the *Nautilus*, construct accommodations and workshops there, undertake the experiments to fully develop his electrical power, and complete his construction drawings. By 1860 when he was ready to begin ordering the components for the *Nautilus*, Captain Nemo's scale drawings would have been taken to a mould-loft, a huge room typically over a hundred yards long, where the plans would be transcribed to full size on the floor. Errors unnoticeable on a small scale thus became visible and correctable. From these, his European suppliers would have crafted full-size wooden "scrive boards," or patterns. The vessel's ribs were made on the bending slab, a pavement of iron dotted with peg-holes. Here was laid the pattern from the scrive board, and pegs were set in holes outlining the pattern. From the furnace came the long red bar of steel. It was thrown on the slab, and with heavy three-pronged forks it was pressed by the shipwrights against the pegs to form the correct curve. The plates, initially formed in massive rolling mills, would be heated again in a furnace for several hours and then bent to their final shape either using a hydraulic press or a heavy cradle, in which the plate could be forced to shape using wedges. Once cooled, the location for each rivet hole would be carefully marked by center-punch and paint. Typically, holes would be formed by huge hydraulic punches, however, given the remote assembly location of the *Nautilus* and the need for extreme precision in fixing the holes, Captain Nemo is likely to have drilled them on-site rather than have them punched at the foundry.[133]

At this point the steel components would have been shipped to Manila, consolidated in a warehouse, and then forwarded on to Captain Nemo's assembly yard on Lincoln Island. The keel was set on wooden blocks in a slipway, and from it the stem, stern, and ribs were set up, so that at this stage the ship looked like a vast metal basket. Riveting plates and ribs first required boring a hole through the two components to be joined. The hole was then reamed — enlarged and aligned — to ensure the rivet would fit, and then the outside was countersunk to accommodate the rivet head. It required two men, working on either side of the plate,

Figure 39: USS Schley *(AA-1 class submarine) under construction at Fore River Shipyard in January 1917*[134]

to insert the hot rivet and hammer it to achieve a compression fit. Finally, the excess would be chiseled off. It was typical to leave a small convex hump on the surface, however, they could be chiseled smooth as was done on the outside surface of *Intelligent Whale*, which is of the same era.[136] Hand riveting would have been necessary, as hydraulic riveting machines of the era could not likely have managed the narrow spaces and curvature of the *Nautilus's* hull. All countersunk rivet heads and all butt and seam straps would be carefully caulked with lead, or a rust joint made by applying a paste made of iron filings, sal-ammoniac, and sulphur, which was a common practice at the time for ensuring tightness in boilers.[137] The sharp edges of the plates would be turned in with a chisel so that the whole hull was watertight and smooth.

The internal, or pressure hull, represented a significant technical challenge. To achieve the necessary performance, it would have to have been of welded construction. Although the electric arc was first discovered in 1802 by Russian scientist Vasily Petrov, and many practical applications including welding were proposed, it was not until 1881 that a Russian inventor, Nikolai Benardos, put the technology to such use.[138] Given Captain Nemo's obvious knowledge and innovation in the field of electricity, we must assume that he independently developed carbon arc welding. Built over a wooden form, sections of hull

*Figure 40: USS **Schley** (AA-1 class submarine) under construction at Fore River Shipyard in April 1917[135]*

*Figure 41: USS **Narwhal** (V-5 / SS-167) under construction at Portsmouth Naval Shipyard in 1927[139]*

Table 6: Early production submarines comparable in size to Verne's *Nautilus*[140]

Vessel	USS *Schley* (SS-52)	USS *Narwhal* (SS-167) USS *Nautilus* (SS-168)	Verne's *Nautilus*
Launched	1918	1928 & 1930	1865
Displacement (surfaced)	1,107 long tons 1,125 t	2,730 long tons 2,770 t	1,358 long tons 1,380 t
Displacement (submerged)	1,482 long tons 1,506 t	3,900 long tons 4,000 t	1,476 long tons 1,500 t
Length	268 ft 9 in 81.92 m	371 ft 113 m	229 ft 8 in 70 m
Beam (hull)	22 ft 10 in 6.96 m	33 ft 3.25 in 10.141 m	26 ft 3 in 8 m
Draft	14 ft 2 in 4.32 m	16 ft 11.25 in 5.163 m	21 ft 6 in 6.55 m

plating and the surrounding stiffening rings would have to have been carefully joined to maintain a high degree of circularity, critical for strength at depth.

It would have been important to stagger weld seams and, where possible, to orient the work to allow welding in the hands-down position to improve the flow into the joint. The precision, cleanliness, and quality of this work needed for this application would have demanded extensive time and attention. The transverse bulkheads, decks, and major tanks would have been formed as part of the pressure hull fabrication. In addition, it's likely that equipment of any significant size would have been installed while still easily accessible during hull construction. Absent advanced inspection techniques, assuring the integrity of the completed hull would have required a pressure test, either using water, assuming the slipway could handle the load, or using air, with its attendant explosive hazard.

By the 1920s, submarines the size of Verne's *Nautilus* (see table 6) were in

production, although welded pressure hulls would not become routine until 1934. Photos (figures 38-42)[141] of these early boats under construction provide a sense of how Captain Nemo's shipbuilding activities on Lincoln Island may have appeared. During World War I, shipyards employing hundreds of workmen were eventually able to shorten production time of these craft to just six months. Considering the number of technologies Captain Nemo was pioneering, and the remote location and limited capacity of his construction facility, it is a valid question whether five years would have been sufficient time for a crew of approximately twenty to have accomplished the work. It may be that Captain Nemo employed many more to assist with the construction of the *Nautilus*, however if true, their fate becomes an open question.

Figure 42: USS Nautilus *(V-6 / SS-168) in 1928*[142]

CONCLUSION

At some point in 1865, with the hull complete, the *Nautilus* would have slid down the slipway and entered the water for the first time. Considerable internal work would still have remained, thus not until late in the year would she be ready to begin her maiden voyage and Captain Nemo divorce his ties to land. It was an eventful year that witnessed the assassination of U.S. President Lincoln and the end of the American Civil War, the crowning of Belgian King Leopold who would go on to brutally exploit the Congo Free State, Jamaica's Morant Bay rebellion, and the beginning of the Paraguayan War, which would prove to be, proportionately, one of the most destructive in modern times. Amidst this dark backdrop, Captain Nemo and his companions put to sea in the *Nautilus* to exact their revenge on imperialism.

"'I love it as though it were my own flesh and blood. In a conventional ship, facing the dangers of the open sea, you feel hazards everywhere. And sometimes, on the surface, your chief sensation is that there's an abyss beneath you...but in the depths, aboard the *Nautilus*, your heart never fails you. No structural weaknesses to worry about, since the double hull has the rigidity of iron. Nor rigging to wear out in the rolling and pitching of the sea. No sails for the winds to carry away. No boilers to be torn apart by steam. No fear of fire since this ship is built of steel not wood. No running low on coal since electricity is our mechanical agent. No chance collision to worry about, since we're all alone down here in the depths of the sea. No tempests to face, because a few meters below the surface, we can find absolute tranquility. There you are, sir, the ship *par excellence*. And if it's true that the engineer has more confidence in the craft than the builder has, and the builder more than the captain himself has, then you can understand the total abandon with which I trust my *Nautilus*! For I am its captain, its builder, and its engineer all in one.'" p. 88

Dear Diane,   6.12.18

After hanging up the phone with you, I remembered these pages of
sketches that my mother had given me when I was boy, shortly after
I discovered Verne's book. They belonged to her uncle who, as I
mentioned, was Pierre Aronnax's manservant for nearly 40 years.
She said her uncle kept them as a reminder of the Professor, who was
haunted by those images and drew them on their voyage back from
Norway. They were found among his papers after his passing. After
hearing about all you have been doing to validate the story and
reconstruct plans for the Nautilus I thought you should have them.

Could it all really
        have been true?

Maelstrom!
   Maelstro

Je suis le droit.
Je suis la justice!
          me dit-il.
Je suis l'opprimé,
     ... et voilà l'oppresseur!

D/S Bergen Jun 1867

Det Bergenske Dampskibsselska

MOBILIS
IN
N
MOBILE

Dieu tout puissant!   Assez! Assez!

Ce ne sont pas de nouveaux continents qu'il faut à la terre,
mais de nouveaux hommes !

Croyez-vous que j'ignore qu'il existe des êtres souffrants,
des races opprimées sur cette terre, des misérables à soulager,
à soulager, des victimes à venger ?
                    Ne comprenez-vous pas ?...

The *Nautilus's* voyage of 20,000 leagues beneath the seas

From November 1867 through June 1868, the *Nautilus*, under the command of Captain Nemo, took Professor Aronnax and his companions on a circumnavigation of the world. They covered a total distance of more than 20,000 leagues, transited the heretofore unknown Arabian Tunnel, and conducted significant exploration of the Southern Ocean, culminating with the first steps taken at the South Pole.

Route of the *Nautilus*

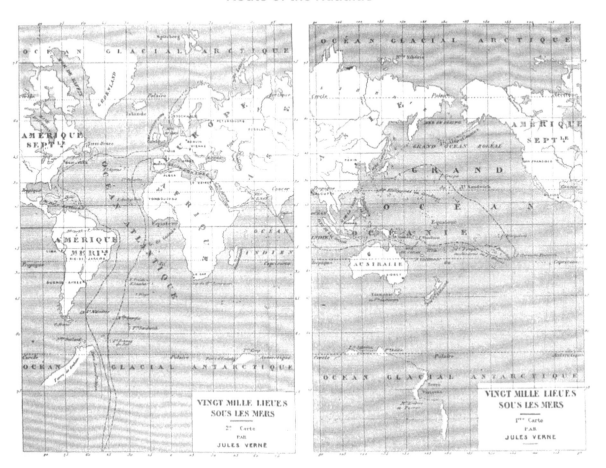

USS *Triton* Completes the First Submerged Circumnavigation[143]

In March 1960, USS *Triton*, powered by two nuclear reactors, became the first (non-fictional) vessel to circumnavigate the world submerged. Retracing the route of the first circumnavigation by Magellan, she covered 26,723 nm (12,372 leagues) in 60 days and 21 hours at an average speed of 18 kts, while crossing the Equator on four different occasions.

The voyage codename was Operation Sandblast.

Route of USS *Triton*

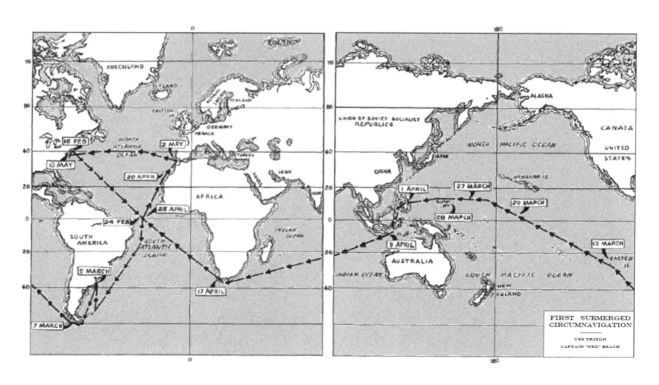

Submarine Development

She was built of steel and was in the form of a cigar, 59 ft long, 6 ft high, and displaced 30 tons. Her battery-powered, 55 horsepower electric motor could drive the boat at 6 knots for 35 miles. She had a periscope for observation, a conventional rudder, and two horizontal planes. To dive, Gymnote filled her ballast tanks until she barely floated, then moving forward, was driven under by her diving planes. Ballast water could be expelled either by means of compressed air or by an electric rotary pump. Gymnote was unable to recharge her batteries while at sea, which restricted her useful range. However, she performed more or less as designed, and proved a useful experimental vessel. She was the first French submarine to be commissioned, appearing on the navy list until 1908.

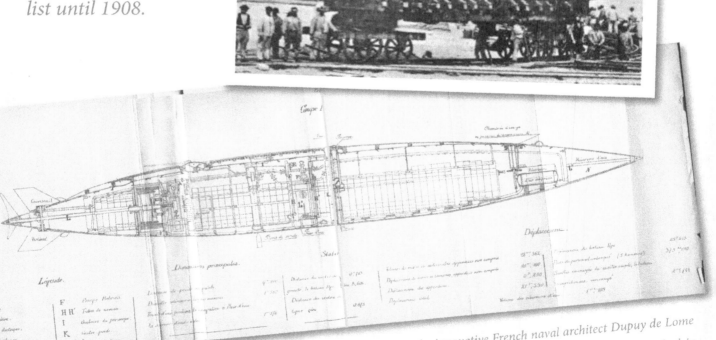

Gymnote was conceived originally by the innovative French naval architect Dupuy de Lome who designed Le Napoleon, the first screw driven, steam powered battleship (launched in 1850). After his death in 1885, work on the submarine was completed by his friend and marine engineer, Gustave Zede. In September 1888, Gymnote was launched in Toulon.

Bibliography & Endnotes

GLOSSARY

afterbody — That part of a hull aft of amidships.

amidships (midships) — (1) Midway (midpoint) between port and starboard sides of a vessel. (2) The midway point between the forward and aft perpendiculars.

athwartships — Lying across the ship from side to side (at right angles to the keel).

auxiliary (machinery) — Vessel's machinery other than the main engine(s).

ballast — Liquid or solid mass loaded in a vessel to improve stability and trim characteristics and to increase propeller immersion. Temporary ballast is usually seawater stored in dedicated tanks. Permanent ballast (if required) is usually solid lead castings.

beam — (1) The registered breadth of a vessel, measured at the outside of the hull amidships, or at its greatest breadth. (2) A transverse structural member supporting a deck and/or strengthening a hull.

bilge — The lowest point of a ship's inner hull, were water is typically collected and removed.

bulkhead — (1) A vertical structural partition dividing a vessel's interior into various compartments for strength and safety purposes; (termed strength bulkhead). (2) Term applied to vertical partition walls (non-structural) subdividing the interior of a vessel into compartments.

butt weld — Full penetration weld joint of two plate edges meeting end-to-end.

center of buoyancy (CB) — The center of mass of the volume of water that the hull of a ship displaces. When a ship is in equilibrium, the center of buoyancy is vertically in-line with the vessel's center of gravity.

center of gravity (CG) — The point within a vessel where all the mass may be assumed to be concentrated. The force of gravity acts vertically downward through this point.

centerline — The longitudinal vertical plane of a vessel.

collapse depth — The submerged depth at which a submarine's hull is expected to collapse due to sea pressure.

compartment — Enclosed space usually with watertight bulkheads, doors or hatches.

companionway — A set of steps leading from a ship's deck down to a cabin or lower deck.

critical point — The point along the longitudinal length of a submarine where an applied vertical force will cause no change in depth but will change the pitch angle (it is aft of the neutral point and moves farther aft with decreasing speed).

critical speed — The speed below which the critical point moves aft of the aft hydroplane.

davit — A crane-like mechanism aboard a ship used to raise or lower a small boat.

design (operating) depth — The maximum depth at which a submarine is allowed to operate under any conditions.

dorade box — A type of vent that permits the passage of air in and out of the cabin or engine room of a boat while keeping rain, spray, and sea wash out.

draft — Depth to which a hull is immersed (this only applies to a submarine when it is on the surface).

duct — Vertical or horizontal large cross-section conduit through which piping or cabling may be run, or fluids (like air) passed.

envelope (form) displacement — The entire volume enclosed by the outer shell of a submarine. Includes submerged and free flood displacement. Important when considering the mass that needs to be propelled or maneuvered. The CG and CB of the envelope displacement volume will be slightly different than for the submerged displacement volume.

floodable volume — The interior volume of the pressure hull minus the volume of all internal equipment and fittings.

forebody — That part of a hull forward of amidships.

frame — Vertical structural component supporting and/or stiffening hull side plating and maintaining the transverse form.

free flood space — Volumes within a vessel that are open to the sea.

free surface effect — The change in stability of a vessel caused by the momentum of liquids moving about freely in a tank or hold.

freeboard — Vertical measurement from the vessel's side amidships from the load waterline to the upper side of the freeboard deck.

freeboard deck — The uppermost complete deck exposed to weather and sea, which has permanent means of weathertight closing of all openings in the exposed part, and below which all openings in the vessel's sides are fitted with permanent means of watertight closing.

galley — Kitchen compartment aboard a vessel.

gangway — A raised platform or walkway providing a passage.

gunwale — The upper edge of the side of a boat or ship.

hard tank — A tank within the pressure hull of a submarine that is exposed to external water pressure.

hatch — Opening in a deck providing access for cargo, personnel, stores, etc.

heel — A temporary rotation about the longitudinal axis (due to the environment or temporary displacement of weight).

hull - The main body or primary part providing strength, buoyancy, and hydrodynamic qualities of a vessel.

keel — Lowest longitudinal strake of plating along the bottom centerline of the hull.

knot — Unit of measure of ship speed equal to one nautical mile per hour (1.1508 mph, 1.852 km/h, 0.5144 m/s).

lightening hole — Large hole cut in a structural member to reduce its weight.

list — A permanent rotation around the longitudinal axis.

main ballast tank — Tanks usually external to the pressure hull that allow major adjustment of the submarine mass in order to submerge.

mess — Space aboard a ship where the crew takes their meals.

metacenter — the point of intersection between a vertical line through the center of buoyancy of a floating body such as a ship, and a vertical line through the new center of buoyancy when the body is heeled, which must be above the center of gravity to ensure stability.

metacentric height — The distance between the center of gravity and the metacenter. For a vessel on the surface of the water, metacentric height (GM) is important, whereas below the surface it is the distance between the center of buoyancy and the center of gravity (BG), which governs the transverse stability of a submarine.

nautical mile — Unit of distance used in marine navigation. (International nautical mile = 1.852 km. 6076.12 ft, 1.1508 land miles.) The international nautical mile is equivalent to the average linear distance over 1 minute of latitude arc at 45° latitude at sea level. (Abbr. nm.)

neutral buoyancy — The condition in which a submerged body will remain suspended at any given depth in a liquid unless affected by some force.

neutral point — The point along the longitudinal length of a submarine at which an applied vertical force causes a depth change but no change in pitch angle.

parallel midbody — Midship portion of a hull within which the longitudinal contour is unchanged.

permanent ballast — Ballast material (usually solid material) that cannot be discharged or transferred by pump or by other means and that which is used for attaining design draft and trim.

pitch — A vessel's motion, rotating about the transverse axis, causing the fore and aft ends to rise and fall repeatedly.

pressure (form) drag — Resistance to motion caused by increased pressure on the front and decreased pressure on the rear of an object moving through a fluid medium.

prismatic coefficient — The ratio of the molded displacement volume to a circumscribing rectangular block produced by the product of the midship-section area and the length.

propeller (screw) — Bladed propulsor generating thrust via the creation of hydrodynamic lift forces in the direction of vessel motion.

propulsion coefficient — The ratio between the indicated horsepower of a ship's engine and the effective horsepower. Describes the efficiency of the stern geometry and the drive train in translating engine power into thrust.

range — The maximum distance a vessel is capable of attaining at its normal service speed without refueling.

reserve buoyancy — Watertight volume of a vessel (or surfaced submarine) above the waterline.

roll — The varying transverse angular motion of a vessel.

rudder — Vertical control surface generating lift or reactionary forces for the directional control of a vessel.

sacrificial anode — Anode of zinc attached to the immersed parts of a hull to prevent deterioration of the hull steel through electrochemical reaction.

sail — The tower-like structure on the topside surface of a submarine. Also known as a fin or fairwater, it acts as a vertical stabilizer when submerged.

section — Transverse vertical plane through the hull perpendicular to the centerline.

skin friction drag — Resistance to motion caused by the viscosity of fluids, and is developed from laminar drag to turbulent drag as a fluid moves on the surface of an object.

soft tank — A tank within the pressure hull of a submarine that is not constructed to withstand external sea pressure.

stability — The state or ability of a vessel afloat to recover equilibrium of trim and heel at sea.

stanchion — Vertical structural supports of bulwarks and safety railings.

stern tube — Sealed and sleeved gland and bearing(s) for through-hull propeller shafting where the shaft penetrates the hull structure.

stiffening ring — a circular structure attached to the inside or outside of pressure vessel to reduce the compressive stress induced in the shell due to external pressure.

submerged (hydrostatic) displacement — The volume of water displaced by a fully submerged submarine. It does not include the mass of fluid in the free flooding spaces.

superstructure — General term for sections of a vessel constructed on and above the upper or main decks of a vessel.

swash bulkhead — Longitudinal or transverse perforated baffle fitted in a tank to reduce free surface effect.

thwart — A structural crosspiece sometimes forming a seat for a rower in a boat.

transverse — Alignment perpendicular to the centerplane of a vessel.

trim — The way in which a ship floats on the water, in relation to her fore-and-aft line, whether on an even keel or down by the head or stern.

trunk — Vertical space or passage formed by bulkheads or casings extending one or more decks, providing access or through which piping or cabling may be conducted.

variable ballast — Ballast material (usually liquid material) that can be discharged or transferred by pump or by other means and used for attaining design draft and trim.

void space — Enclosed space (often watertight) intentionally left empty.

watertight — Capable of preventing the ingress of water under a head of water likely to occur in the intact or damaged condition.

windlass — Winch designed for the raising and lowering of an anchor.

SUBMARINE DESIGN BIBLIOGRAPHY

For those wishing to investigate in greater depth the fascinating challenges associated with submarine design, I have included a short bibliography of references that were most useful in my development of the *Nautilus* and should prove accessible to the general reader. The list includes some older titles, seldom referenced in modern design, but they provide insight into the difficulties of early submarine construction and the nascent approaches taken to address them. Not only is this relevant to the *Nautilus*, but it also allows us to appreciate the prescience of Jules Verne. It is also true that the field of submarine design has increasingly become classified and thus not within the public realm. Nonetheless, these sources should be sufficient to launch your design ambitions.

Books

Alden, John (Commander). *The Fleet Submarine in the U.S. Navy: A Design and Construction History*. United States Naval Institute. Annapolis, MD. 1979.

Allmendinger, Eugene. *Submersible Vehicle System Design*. The Society of Naval Architects and Marine Engineers. Jersey City, NJ. 1990.

Burcher, Roy & Louis Rydill. *Concepts in Submarine Design*. Cambridge University Press, Cambridge, UK, 1994.

Burgoyne, Alan H. *Submarine Navigation Past and Present*. Grant Richards, London and E.P. Dutton and Company, New York. 1903.

Busby, Frank. *Manned Submersibles*. Office of the Oceanographer of the Navy. 1976.

Cable, Frank T. *The Birth and Development of the American Submarine*. Harper and Brothers, New York, NY. 1924.

Corbin, Thomas W. *The Romance of Submarine Engineering*. J.B. Lippencott Co. Philadelphia. 1913.

Daniels, R.J. *The End of an Era: Memoirs of a Naval Constructor*. Periscope Publishing LTD. Cornwall, UK. © 2003.

Friedman, Norman. *Submarine Design and Development*. Conway Maritime Press Limited, London, UK, 1984.

Gabler, Ulrich. *Submarine Design*. Bernard & Graefe, Koblenz, Germany. 1986.

Hay, Marley F. *Secrets of the Submarine*. Dodd, Mead and Company, Inc. New York, NY. 1917.

Hoar, Allen. *The Submarine Torpedo Boat, Its Characteristics and Modern Development*. D. Van Nostrand Company. New York, NY. 1916.

Hovgaard, G.W. *Submarine Boats*. E.&F. Spon, 125, Strand, London. 1887.

Kormilitsin, Y.N. and O.A. Khalizev. *The Theory of Submarine Design*. St. Petersburg Maritime Technical University. St. Petersburg. 2001.

Manstan, Roy R. and Frederic J. Frese. *Turtle: David Bushell's Revolutionary Vessel*. Westholme Publishing. Yardley, PA. 2010.

Morris, Richard K. *John P. Holland, Inventor of the Modern Submarine*. United States Naval Institute. Annapolis, MD. 1966.

Renilson, Martin. *Submarine Hydrodynamics*. Springer International Publishing. 2015.

Sueter, Murray F. *The Evolution of the Submarine Boat, Mine and Torpedo*. Gieve's, Matthews and Seagrove, Ltd. The Hard, Portsmouth. 1907.

Weir, Gary. *Building American Submarines, 1914-1940*. University Press of the Pacific. Honolulu, HI. 2000.

Zim, Herbert S. *Submarines, The Story of Undersea Boats*. Harcourt, Brace and Company, New York, NY. 1942.

Papers

Andersen Poul, Jens J. Kappel, and Eugen Spangenberg. "Aspects of Propeller Development for Submarines." Presented at the First International Symposium on Marine Propulsors, Trondheim, Norway, June 2009.

Arentzen, E.S. and Philip Mandel. "Naval Architectural Aspects of Submarine Design." Presented at the Annual Meeting of the Society of Naval Architects and Marine Engineers, November 17-18, 1960, New York, NY.

Bedell, C. H. "The Submarine." *Universal Engineer* Vol XXXV, pp. 17-25. January 1922.

Benford, Harry. "In Tribute to Riveted Ships." Presented to the Great Lakes & Great Rivers Section, Society of Naval Architects & Marine Engineers. 24 September 2009.

Brown, D. K. "Submarine Pressure Hull Design and Diving Depth Between the Wars." *Warship International*, No. 3, 1987.

Dallinger, J. Frederick and J.E. McGill. "Submarine High-Pressure Air System." Presented at the Annual Meeting of the Society of Naval Architects and Marine Engineers, November 15-16, 1962, New York, NY.

French, Peter D. "The Role of Diesel Engines in Early Submarine Development." USMC Command and Staff College. Quantico, VA. 2010.

Gertler, Morton. "Resistance experiments on a systematic series of streamlined bodies of revolution—for application to the design of high-speed submarines." DTMB Report C-297, Naval Ship Research and Development Centre, Washington D.C., April 1950.

Hay, Marley. "The Design of Submarines." Presented at the Annual Meeting of the Society of Naval Architects and Marine Engineers, November 18-19, 1909, New York, NY.

Hitchcock, Peter Winston. "Intelligent Whale: A Historical and Archaeological Analysis of an American Civil War Submersible."

Jackson, Harry A. "Fundamentals of Submarine Concept Design." *SNAME Transactions*, Vol. 100, 1992, pp. 419-448.

Johnson, David. "A Visual Guide to the S-class Submarines Part I." June, 2011 and "A Visual Guide to U.S. Fleet Submarines Part II and III" 2010 & 2012.

Joubert, P. N. "Some Aspects of Submarine Design Part 1—Hydrodynamics, and Part 2—Shape of Submarine." Defense Science and Technology Organisation Technical Report DSTO-TR-1622, October 2004 and December 2006.

Hemsley, R. "HVAC Considerations for Small SSK Submarine Design." BMT Defense Services Ltd. Bath, UK. 2015.

Land, E.S. "Submarine Hulls." Presented at the Annual Meeting of the Society of Naval Architects and Marine Engineers, November 15-16, 1917, New York, NY.

MacKay, John. "Structural Analysis and Design of Pressure Hulls: the State of the Art and Future Trends." Defense R&D Canada Technical Memorandum. October 2007.

McGill, J.E. "The Design of Air Conditioning and Ventilation Systems for Nuclear Submarines." Presented at the New England section of the Society of Naval Architects and Marine Engineers, January 1959.

McKee, Andrew Irwin. "Recent Submarine Design Practices and Problems." Presented at the Annual Meeting of the Society of Naval Architects and Marine Engineers, November 12-13, 1959, New York, NY.

Pohler, C. H., A. A. Bernent, D. S. Wilson, and W. A. Skinner. "Submarine Main Ballast Tanks—Theory and Methods for Refined Structural Design." *Marine Technology*, April 1969.

Robertson, I. M. "Analytical Calculations of Fatigue Loading of Submarine Hulls." MRL Technical Report. Victoria, Australia. 1990.

Stachiw, J.D. and J. R. McKay. "Windows for External or Internal Hydrostatic Pressure Vessels—Part VII." Technical Report R773. Naval Civil Engineering Laboratory. Port Hueneme, CA. August 1972.

Torkelson, Kai Oscar. "Comparative Naval Architectural Analysis of Diesel Submarines." Massachusetts Institute of Technology, June 2005.

Wilgenhof, J.D., J.J. Conesa Giménez, and J. García Peláez. "Performance of Ballast Tank Blowing System." Presented at the Undersea Defense Technology Conference, Cartagena, Spain. 2011.

Standards

"System Certification Procedures and Criteria Manual for Deep Submergence Systems," Revision A (SS800-AG-MAN-010/P-9290). Naval Sea Systems Command, Department of the Navy. Washington, D.C. 1988.

"Rules for Classification and Construction, Naval Ship Technology, Sub-Surface Ships," Germanischer Lloyd Aktiengesellschaft. Hamburg. 2008.

"Rules for the Classification of Naval Submarines." Bureau Veritas. Neuilly sur Seine Cedex, France. September 2016

Websites

The Fleet Type Submarine, NAVPERS 16160.
Available at: https://maritime.org/doc/fleetsub/

19TH-CENTURY SUBMARINE DEVELOPMENT

The history of the submarine, from a practical standpoint, is largely a 20th-century story. Not unlike the airplane, it is a technology that came of age in the crucible of the First World War, attained lethal maturity in the Second World War, and then experienced a major technological disruption that re-invented it in its modern form. In the case of aviation, that revolutionary innovation was the jet engine, for submarines it was nuclear power. But the lesser-known story of submarine development prior to its official adoption by French and American navies at the turn of the century is a fascinating story of creativity spurred by the imagination and wars of a different era. The following sources offer rich rewards to those interested in undertaking this exploration.

Baird, G.W. "Submarine Torpedo Boats." *Naval Engineers Journal*. August 1902.

Barber, F.M. "Lecture on Submarine Boats and Their Application to Torpedo Operations." U.S. Torpedo Station, Newport Rhode Island. 1875.

Barnes, J.S. *Submarine Warfare Offensive and Defensive*. Van Nostrand. New York, NY. 1869.

Bishop, Farnham. *The Story of the Submarine*. The Century Company, New York, NY. 1916.

Bushnell, David. "General Principles and Construction of a Sub-marine Vessel." Transactions of the American Philosophical Society 4. Philadelphia, PA. 1799.

Burgoyne, Alan H. *Submarine Navigation Past and Present*. 2 vols. E.P. Dutton and Company, New York. 1903.

Corbin, Thomas W. *The Romance of Submarine Engineering*. J.B. Lippencott Co. Philadelphia. 1913.

Delgado, James P. *Misadventures of a Civil War Submarine: Iron, Guns, and Pearls*. Texas A&M University Press, College Station, TX. © 2012.

Field, Cyril. *The Story of the Submarine From the Earliest Ages to the Present Day*. J.B. Lippencott Co. Philadelphia. 1908.

Forest, F. and H. Noalhat. *Les Bateaux Sous-Marines Historique*. Ch. Dunod, Editor. Paris, France. 1900.

Fulton, Robert. *Torpedo War, and Submarine Explosions*. William Elliot. New York, NY. 1810.

Fyfe, Herbert C. *Submarine Warfare, Past and Present*. E. Grant Richards, London, UK. 1907.

Gaget, M. *La Navigation Sous-Marine Généralités et Historique*. Librairie Polytechnique. Paris, France. 1901.

González, Agustín Ramón Rodríguez. *Isaac Peral: Historia de una Frustración*. Ayuntamiento de Cartegena. 1993.

Hennebert, Eugène. *Les Torpilles*. Librairie Hachette Et Cie. Paris, France. 1888.

Hicks, Brian. *Sea of Darkness: Unraveling the Mysteries of the HL Hunley*. Spry Publishing. Ann Arbor, MI. 2014.

Hovgaard, G.W. *Submarine Boats*. E.&F.N. Spon. London, UK. 1887.

Laubeuf, M. *Sous Marins et Submersibles*. Librairie Delagrave. Paris, France. 1915.

Manstan, Roy R. and Frederic J. Frese. *Turtle: David Bushell's Revolutionary Vessel*. Westholme Publishing. Yardley, PA. 2010.

Melville, George W. "The Submarine Boat: Its Promises and Performances." *The North American Review*. Vol CLXXII, No. 533. April 1901.

Monturiol, Narciso. *Ensayo Sobre El Arte de Navegar Por Debajo del Agua*. Barcelona. 1891.

Morris, Richard K. *John P. Holland, Inventor of the Modern Submarine*. USNI. Annapolis, MD. 1966.

Parsons, William Barclay. *Robert Fulton and the Submarine*. Columbia University Press. New York, NY. 1922.

Pesce, G. L. *La Navigation Sous-Marine*. Librairie de Sciences Generales. Paris. 1897.

Ragan, Mark K. *Submarine Warfare in the Civil War*. Da Capo Press. Cambridge, MA. 1999.

Roland, Alex. *Underwater Warfare in the Age of Sail*. Indiana University Press. Bloomington, IN. 1978.

Sleeman, C. *Torpedoes and Torpedo Warfare*. Griffin & Co. Portsmouth, UK. 1889.

Sonrel, L. *The Bottom of the Sea*. Translated by Elihu Rich. Scribner, Armstrong & Co. New York, NY. 1872.

Stewart, Matthew. *Monturiol's Dream: The Extraordinary Story of the Submarine Inventor Who Wanted to Save the World*. Pantheon Books. New York, NY. 2003.

CITATIONS

(Note: images used are original or in the public domain unless otherwise noted.)

Citation for the George Washington quotation: From George Washington to Thomas Jefferson, 26 September 1785, Founders Online, National Archives, last modified June 29, 2017, http://founders.archives.gov/documents/Washington/04-03-02-0251. [Original source: *The Papers of George Washington, Confederation Series*, vol. 3, 19 May 1785–31 March 1786, ed. W. W. Abbot. Charlottesville: University Press of Virginia, 1994, pp. 279–283.]

Plongeur drawings taken from: Paris, Edmond (Vice Admiral). L'art naval à l'exposition universelle de Paris en 1867: augmenté des derniers perfectionnements et inventions maritimes jusqu'en 1869. Description from: Hovgaard, G.W. *Submarine Boats*. E.&F. Spon, 125, Strand, London. 1887.

[1] Illustrations from Har'El, Zvi, "The Illustrated Jules Verne." Zvi Har'El's Jules Verne Collection. 29 Aug. 2008. Web. 12 Dec. 2012.

[2] Crisafulli, Michael. "The Vernian Era." Web. 18 Dec. 2012. <http://www.vernianera.com >

[3] "The Winans Steamer in Course of Construction At Baltimore." *Scientific American* Vol XIV, Issue 9. New York, NY. November 5, 1858 and "The Latest Yankee Experiment in Naval Architecture." *Scientific American* Vol 1013, Issue 11. p. 168. September 9, 1865.

[4] Winans, Ross and Thomas Winans. "Hull of Steam Vessels." U.S. Patent 21917. 26 Oct 1958.

[5] Joubert, P. N. "Some Aspects of Submarine Design Part 1—Hydrodynamics, and Part 2—Shape of Submarine." Defense Science and Technology Organisation Technical Report DSTO-TR-1622, October 2004 and December 2006.

[6] Gertler, Morton. "Resistance experiments on a systematic series of streamlined bodies of revolution—for application to the design of high-speed submarines." DTMB Report C-297, Naval Ship Research and Development Centre, Washington D.C., April 1950.

[7] Burcher, Roy & Louis Rydill, *Concepts in Submarine Design*. Cambridge University Press, Cambridge, U.K., 1994, p. 56 & 105.

[8] Arentzen, E.S. and Philip Mandel. "Naval Architectural Aspects of Submarine Design." Presented at the Annual Meeting of the Society of Naval Architects and Marine Engineers, November 17-18, 1960, New York, NY.

[9] McKee, Andrew Irwin. "Recent Submarine Design Practices and Problems." Presented at the Annual Meeting of the Society of Naval Architects and Marine Engineers, November 12-13, 1959, New York, NY.

[10] Sea State Codes, World Meteorological Organization. 12 Dec. 2012.

[11] See note 7, above.

[12] See note 7, above.

[13] Reed, E. J. *Shipbuilding in Iron and Steel*. William Clowes and Sons, London, UK. 1869.

[14] Hearn, Chester. *The Capture of New Orleans 1862*. Louisiana State University Press. Baton Rouge, LA. ©1995.

[15] Pope, Franklin Leonard. "The Electric Motor and its Applications." *Scribner's Magazine*. Vol III (January—June). Charles Scribner's Sons. New York, NY. 1888.

[16] Joule, J.P. "On the Fusion of Metals by Voltaic Electricity." Originally presented March 4, 1856. *The Scientific Papers of James Prescott Joule* published by The Physical Society of London. London, UK. 1884.

[17] Harding, Richard. *The Royal Navy 1930-2000, Innovation and Defense*. Frank Cass. London, UK. 2005; "British Rivetless Ship." *The Journal of the American Society of Mechanical Engineers*. Vol 42. ASME. New York, NY. 1920.

[18] "Principles of Ship Performance." EN400 Course Notes. United States Naval Academy. Annapolis, MD. 2017.

[19] "Great Eastern Monster Ship." York Herald. 17 January 1857; Gillings, Annabel. *Brunel*. Haus Publishing Limited. London, UK. ©2006; Dugan, James. *The Great Iron Ship*. Harper and Brothers. New York, NY. ©1953.

[20] Lottman, Herbert R. *Jules Verne: An Exploratory Biography*. St. Martin's Press, New York, NY. ©1996.

[21] Woods Hole Oceanographic Institution. "Marine Fouling and its Prevention." U.S. Naval Institute. Annapolis, MD. 1952. George Banta Publishing Co., Menasha, WI.

[22] Young, Charles F. *The Fouling and Corrosion of Iron Ships*. The London Drawing Association. London, UK. 1867.

[23] Graham, Daniel P. "Some Factors in the Use of Plastic Ship-Bottom Paints by the United States Navy." SNAME. 1947.

24 Stachiw, J.D. and J. R. McKay. "Windows for External or Internal Hydrostatic Pressure Vessels — Part VII." Technical Report R773. Naval Civil Engineering Laboratory. Port Hueneme, CA. August 1972.

25 Beebe, William. *Half Mile Down*. Harcourt, Brace and Company, New York, NY. ©1934. Appendix B by Otis Barton.

26 *Electrical Review*, Vol 64. April 18, 1914. pp. 761-762.

27 Jackson, Harry A. "Fundamentals of Submarine Concept Design." SNAME Transactions, Vol. 100, 1992, pp. 419-448.

28 Carlton, John. *Marine Propellers and Propulsion*. Elsevier Ltd. Oxford, U.K., 2012. pp. 1-9.

29 "Ironclad Warships." Wikipedia: The Free Encyclopedia. Wikimedia Foundation, Inc. 18 Dec. 2012. Web.

30 Collins, J.W. "The Beam Trawling Fishery of Great Britain, with Notes of Beam-Trawling in other European Countries, etc." Bulletin of the United States Fish Commission.

31 https://www.learneasy.info/mdme/memmods/mem30009a/lifting_systems/Ingersoll_drum_calculator.html. Web. 18 Dec. 2012.

32 Patents for Inventions. Abridgement of Specifications, Relating to Electricity and Magnetism, Their Generation and Application. Part II. 1858-1866. Office of the Commissioners of Patents for Inventions, London. 1874. Google Books, accessed 24 January 2018.

33 Wong, J. I. (2016, October 5). "The story of the humble latex, which laid the foundation for the global web." Retrieved 2017, December 12 from Quartz website: https://qz.com/785119/the-forgotten-tropical-tree-sap-that-set-off-a-victorian-tech-boom-and-gave-us-global-telecommunications/.

34 "Arc Lamps." Edison Tech Center. Web. 9 Oct 2015. http://www.edisontechcenter.org/ArcLamps.html.

35 Gendre, Maxime. "Two Centuries of Electric Light Source Innovations." Eindhoven University of Technology, Department of Applied Physics. Eindhoven, Netherlands. Retrieved 9 Oct 2015.

36 Chance, James F., *The Lighthouse Work of Sir James Chance*. Baronet, Smith, Elder & Co., London, UK, 1902, pp. 83-98.

37 Hoar, Allen. *The Submarine Torpedo Boat: Its Characteristics and Modern Development*. D. Van Nostrand Co. New York, NY. 1916.

38 "Correspondence of M. Jerome Nickles, dated Paris, June 28, 1854." *The American Journal of Science and Arts*. Vol XVIII — November 1854. (B. Stillman, Ed.) G.P. Putnam and Co. New York, NY. 1854; Niaudet, Alfred. *Elemental Treatise on Electric Batteries*. John Wiley and Sons. New York, NY. 1890; Rindskopf, Mike H. *Steel Boats, Iron Men: History of the U.S. Submarine Force*. Turner Publishing Company. Nashville, TN. 1994.

39 Hovgaard, G.W. *Submarine Boats*. E.&F. Spon, 125, Strand, London. 1887.

40 See note 39, above.

41 "The Voyage of Bounty's Launch." Pitcairn Islands Study Center. Pacific Union College. Web. 12 Dec. 2012.

42 Buker, G. E. *The Metal Life Car: The Inventor, the Impostor, and the Business of Lifesaving*. Tuscaloosa: The University of Alabama Press. ©2008.

43 Gurney, Alan. *Compass: A Story of Exploration and Innovation*. W.W. Norton and Co. New York, NY. ©2005.

44 Bolton, H.C. and I.D. Rae. "The Admiral's Storm Glass." *Weather*. Vol 47. 1992.

45 Biographical summaries excerpted from associated Wikipedia entries. Web. 11 Nov 2017.

46 "Jefferson's Legacy — A Brief History of the Library of Congress." https://www.loc.gov/legacy/loc.html. Web. 9 Jan. 2013.

47 "http://www.bpl.org/general/history.html. Web. 10 Jan. 2013; Lydenberg, Harry Miller. "History of the New York Public Library." Astor, Lennex and Tilden Foundation. New York, NY. ©1923.

48 Favier, Jean and Mireille M. Dedios. "The History of the French National Library." *Daedalus* 124, no. 4 (1996).

49 Miles, Wyndham D. "The Velvet-Lined Gas Mask of John Stenhouse." *Armed Forces Chemical Journal*, 1958, 12(3):24-25.

50 Butcher, William, *Jules Verne: The Definitive Biography*. Thunder Mouth Press, New York, NY. 2006, 2008.

51 Gilbert, Darrell. "History of the Fire Hose." Crownshoptalk.com. Web. 11 Nov 2017.

52 Log Book of HMS Resolution. Cambridge Digital Library. 23 Feb 2016. Web.

53 *Marine Engineering Vol IV*. Aldrich and Donaldson, New York, NY. © 1899.

54 "Distillation of Seawater." https://maritime.org/doc/fleetsub.hmtl. 23 Feb 2016. Web.

55 "Improved Electrical Heating Apparatus." Google patents. Google. Retrieved October 21, January 2018.

56 Gantz, Carroll. *Refrigeration: A History*. McFarland and Co. Jefferson, NC. ©2015.

57 McGill, J.E. "The Design of Air Conditioning and Ventilating Systems for Nuclear Submarines." Paper presented at the January 1959 meeting of the New England section of The Society of Naval Architects and Marine Engineers.

58 Corbin, Thomas W. *The Romance of Submarine Engineering*. J.B. Lippencott Co. Philadelphia. 1913.

59 See note 39, above.

60 Grant, Benjamin P. "Density as a Cost Driver in Naval Submarine Procurement." Naval Postgraduate School. Monterey, CA. June 2008.

61 "Submarine Air Quality." National Academy Press. ©1998; "Submarine Atmosphere Control Manual." (Unclassified excerpt of NAVSEA S 9510-AB-ATM-010). U.S. Naval Sea Systems Command. Washington, DC; "U.S. Navy Diving Manual. Rev 7." (SS521-AG-P20-010). Naval Sea Systems Command. Washington, DC. Dec 2016.

62 See note 20, above.

63 Broich, John. *Squadron: Ending the African Slave Trade*. Overlook Press. 2017.

64 Marx, Robert F. *The History of Underwater Exploration*. Dover Publications, New York, NY 1990, pp. 90-93.

65 "Will Your Next Dive be 3 Hours Long?: Everything You Need to Know About Rebreathers." *African Expedition Magazine*. Vol 5, Issue 2. 2013.

66 Brubakk, Alf and Tom Neuman. *Bennett and Elliotts' Physiology and Medicine of Diving*. Saunders Ltd. Philadelphia, PA. 2003.

67 Emsley, John. *Nature's Building Blocks: An A-Z Guide to the Elements*. Oxford University Press. Oxford, UK. ©2001.

68 Wienke, B. R. *Technical Diving in Depth*. Best Publishing Co. Flagstaff, AZ. 2001; Abraini, J. H., M. C. Gardette-Chaufour, E. Martinez, J. C. Roustain, C. Lemaire. "Psychophysiological reactions in humans during an open sea dive to 500 m with a hydrogen-helium-oxygen mixture." *Journal of Applied Physiology*. American Physiological Society. 76 (3): 1113-8. 1994.

69 Schechner, Sara J. "The Art of Making Leyden Jars and Batteries according to Benjamin Franklin." eRittenhouse 26. 2015.

70 Whitman, Edward. "The Submarine Technology of Jules Verne," *Undersea Warfare Magazine*, Winter, 2004.

71 Pope, Franklin Leonard. "The Electric Motor and its Applications." *Scribner's Magazine*. Vol III (January – June). Charles Scribner's Sons. New York, NY. 1888; Schiffer, Michael Brian. *Power Struggles. Scientific Authority and the Creation of Practical Electricity before Edison*. MIT Press. Cambridge, MA. 2008; Page, Charles G. "Improvement in Electromagnetic Engines." (Patent 104080) U.S. Patent Office, Washington, DC. 1854.

72 Jensen, William B. "Captain Nemo's Battery, Chemistry and the Science Fiction of Jules Verne," *Chemical Intelligencer*, 1997.

73 See note 72, above.

74 Yeager, Ernst B. "The Sodium Amalgam-Oxygen Continuous Feed Cell." In *Fuel Cells*, Mitchell, W. (Ed.), Academic Press, New York City, 1963, Chap. 7, pp. 299-328.

75 Reif-Acherman, Simón. "Heinrich Geissler: Pioneer of Electrical Science and Vacuum Technology." *Proceedings of the IEEE 2015*. pp. 1672-1684.

76 Speight, James. *Chemical and Process Design Handbook*. McGraw-Hill. New York, NY. ©2002.

77 Polmar, Norman and Kenneth Moore. *Cold War Submarines: The Design and Construction of U.S. and Soviet Submarines*. Potomac Books, Inc. Washington, DC. ©2004.

78 "The Albacore Story: Concept to Mothballs." http://www.ussalbacore.org.html. 23 Dec 2014. Web.

79 See note 77, above.

80 See note 67, above.

81 Web. 20 Mar 2014. http://www.atomicarchive.com/Photos/CP1/index.shtml.

82 "Sub-marine Boat." *American Railroad Journal and Advocate of Internal Improvements*. January – July. Published by D.K. Minor Editor and Proprietor. New York, NY. 1883; "The Hunt for the Alligator." The Navy and Marine Living History Association. http://www.navyandmarine.org/alligator. Accessed 12 Dec. 2012; "The Hunt for the Alligator." NOAA. Web. 12 Dec. 2012.

83 Hicks, Brian. *Sea of Darkness: Unraveling the Mysteries of H.L. Hunley*. Spry Publishing. Ann Arbor, MI. ©2014.

84   See note 39, above.

85   "The Hunt for the Alligator." The Navy and Marine Living History Association. http://www.navyandmarine. org/alligator. Accessed 12 Dec. 2012.

86   Martine, Charles-Noel. *La Vie et l'oeuvre de Jules Verne*. Paris, Michel de l'Omeraie. 1978. p. 176.

87   See note 20, above.

88   Stewart, Matthew. *Monturiol's Dream: The Extraordinary Story of the Submarine Inventor Who Wanted to Save the World*. Pantheon Books, New York, NY ©2003.

89   Hughes, Robert, *Barcelona*. Alfred A. Knopf, Inc. New York, NY. ©1992.

90   See note 88, above.

91   Courtesy of Flemming Mahler Larsen. Retrieved from "Ictineo II." Wikipedia: The Free Encyclopedia. Wikimedia Foundation, Inc. 11 Oct. 2015. Web. 5 Nov. 2015.

92   David, Saul. *The Indian Mutiny: 1857*. Viking. New York, NY. 2002; Dalrymple, William. *The Last Mughal: The Fall of a Dynasty, Delhi 1857*. Bloomsbury Publishing. London, UK. ©2006.

93   Turnbull, C.M. *A History of Modern Singapore: 1819-2005*. National University of Singapore Press. Singapore. 2009.

94   Pern, B.R. *A History of Rangoon*. American Baptist Mission Press. Rangoon. 1939.

95   Carroll, John M. *A Concise History of Hong Kong*. Rowman & Littlefield Publishers, Inc. Lanham, MD. 2007.

96   Hughes, Robert. *The Fatal Shore: The Epic of Australia's Founding*. Alfred A. Knopf. New York. 1986.

97   Belich, James. *Making Peoples: A History of the New Zealanders From Polynesian Settlement to the End of the Nineteenth Century*. University of Hawaii Press. Honolulu, HI. 1996.

98   Goscha, Christopher. *Vietnam: A New History*. Basic Books. New York, NY. 2016.

99   Wyatt, David K. *Thailand: A Short History*. 2nd Edition. Yale University Press. New Haven, CT 2003.

100   Abeyasekere, Susan. *Jakarta: A History*. Oxford University Press. Oxford, UK. 1987.

101   "On the Muelle Del Ray" by John Tewell. License CC BY-NC 2.0, https://www.flickr.com/photos/ johntewell/5779008136/in/photostream/.

102   Foreman, John. *The Philippine Islands*. Charles Scribner and Sons. New York, NY. 1899.

103   Rand, Sturgis. "The Romance of Christmas Island." *McClure's Magazine*. Vol XVIII (November 1901 to April 1902). S.S. McClure Co. New York, NY. 1902.

104   Sailing Directions (enroute) South China Sea and the Gulf of Thailand. Pub. 161. National Geospatial-Intelligence Agency, Springfield, VA. 2017; "The China Sea Directory Vol II: Containing Directions for the Navigation of the China Sea Between Singapore and Hong Kong." 4th edition. Hydrographic Office, Admiralty, London, UK. 1899.

105   Map of South China Sea taken from CIA World Factbook. Web. 12 Dec 2012.

106   Image of Lincoln Island from Google Maps. 12 Dec. 2012.

107   Stone, Peter. *The Canary Islands: A Cultural History*. Signal Books. Oxford, UK. 2015.

108   Web. 9 Oct. 2015. <http://www.centrosturisticos.com/centros/CENTROS/published_en/DEFAULT/ node_2036_2201.html>

109   "Creusot Steam Hammer." The American Society of Mechanical Engineers. New York, NY. September 16, 1982.

110   See note 109, above.

111   "Penydarren Ironworks." <http://www.alangeorge.co.uk/Images3_I/Penydarren_Ironworks_ByRobertCraw-shay_1875.JPG>

112   Wilkins, Charles. "The History of Merthyr Tydfil." Harry Wood Southey. Merthyr Tydfil, UK. 1867; "Richard Trevithick." Wikipedia: The Free Encyclopedia. Wikimedia Foundation, Inc. 18 Dec. 2012. Web. 18 Dec. 2012; Burton, Anthony. *Richard Trevithick: Giant of Steam*. Aurum Press Ltd. London, UK. 2000.

113   Hollett, D. *Men of Iron: Story of Cammell Laird Shipbuilders, 1828-1991*. Countyvise Ltd. Birkenhead, UK. 1992.

114   "A Rich Company Heritage." Motala Verkstad. Web. 12 Dec. 2012.

115   "Two Centuries of Shipbuilding." By the Scotts at Greenock. Offices of Engineering. London, UK. 1906.

[116] See note 108, above.

[117] Web. 12 Dec. 2012. <http://www.oldbookillustrations.com/pages/crampton-locomotive.php?lng=en>

[118] Web. 12 Dec. 2012. <http://vrc-cbe-uw.blogspot.com/2008/06/galerie-des-machines-paris-1889-iron-or.html>

[119] See note 118, above.

[120] http://img178.imageshack.us/img178/9519/crampton1qk2.jpg. Web. 31 Dec/ 2012.

[121] Manchester, William. *The Arms of Krupp: The Rise and Fall of the Industrial Dynasty That Armed Germany at War.* Little, Brown and Company. Boston, MA. 1968.

[122] See note 114, above.

[123] Bessermer, Henry. *Sir Henry Bessember, An Autobiography.* Offices of the Engineer. London, UK ©1905.

[124] "Gurley Historical Sketch." http://www.gurley.com. Accessed 18 Dec. 2012.

[125] Officer, Lawrence and Samuel Williamson. "Measuring Worth." Web ©2011. 28 Dec. 2012.

[126] Requard, Georges. "The Currency of France." Selections from *The Numismatist*, Modern Foreign Currency. The American Numismatic Association. Whitman Publishing Co. Racine, WI. ©1961.

[127] "French Franc." Wikipedia: The Free Encyclopedia. Wikimedia Foundation, Inc. 27 Dec. 2012. Web. 31 Dec 2012.

[128] See note 125, above.

[129] Submarine images from U.S. National Archives, courtesy of Navsource Online. www.navsource.org. Web. 12 Dec 2012.

[130] Web. 12 Dec. 2012. <http://www.portcities.org.uk/london/server/show/ConNarrative.59/chapterId/1024/Thames-Ironworks.html>

[131] Web. 17 Dec 2012. <http://www.sheffieldforgemasters.com/sfm/overview/history/1800s >

[132] "Ironclad Warships." Wikipedia: The Free Encyclopedia. Wikimedia Foundation, Inc. 18 Dec. 2012. Web. 18 Dec. 2012.

[133] Sackett, Terrance. "Ship Building in the 19th Century." http://ezinearticles.com/?Ship-Building-in-the-19th-Century&id=4580546; Brown, David. *Warrior to Dreadnought: Warship Development, 1860-1905.* Chatham Publishing, London. ©1997.

[134] See note 129, above.

[135] See note 129, above.

[136] Hitchock, Peter Winston. "Intelligent Whale: A Historical and Archaeological Analysis of an American Civil War Submersible."

[137] Alban, Ernst. *The High-Pressure Steam Engine Investigated.* W. Hughes, King's Head Court, Gough Square, 1848.

[138] Cary, Howard. *Modern Welding Technology* (6th edition). Pearson/Prentice Hall. Upper Saddle River, NJ. ©2004.

[139] See note 129, above.

[140] Bauer, K. Jack and Stephen S. Roberts. *Register of Ships of the U.S. Navy, 1775-1990: Major Combatants.* Greenwood Press. New York, NY. 1991.

[141] See note 129, above.

[142] See note 129, above.

[143] Beach, Edward L. *Around the World Submerged: The Voyage of the Triton.* Naval Institute Press. Annapolis, MD. 1962.

[144] Lake, Simon. *Submarine: The Autobiography of Simon Lake as told to Herbert Corey.* D. Appleton-Century Company, Inc. New York, NY. 1938.

ACKNOWLEDGMENTS

To Jules Verne must go the credit for creating an original work and our appreciation for giving the world the gift of his imagination. No matter how painstakingly executed, these plans can never be more than a derivative.

Like Verne and his publisher Hetzel, my collaboration with Brad Pauquette has provided the means to bring my creation to the public in finished form. His talented publishing and marketing team, especially Cate Labish, taught me what it takes to make an idea into a book.

I appreciate the ambition of Google Books to democratize knowledge, which made so many obscure 19th century technical references available to me. In addition, I applaud Wikipedia's vision of empowering and engaging people around the world to collect and develop educational content under free license or in the public domain and disseminate it effectively. Though often derided as a serious source, I cannot deny its utility in guiding my research.

Verne's landmark novel may have inspired my underwater fantasies as a child, but the United States Navy allowed me to live them out. I have tremendous respect for, and owe a debt of gratitude to, the U.S. Submarine Force, an organization of excellence that has given me whatever semblance of credibility I have to write on this subject.

In any work of the creative arts, there is the potential, through collaboration, to realize a richer and more robust outcome than even the most inspired original visions. It has been beyond good fortune to have been able to lean on the expertise of Brad Thomas, a superb engineer with a superior imagination, who diligently allowed me to erase the line separating fact from fiction in creating the *Nautilus*.

These plans, depicting the design of Verne's submarine, represent the culmination of an idea that really began over forty years ago. Thanks go to my parents for equipping my imagination with lots of graph paper, and of course, fueling it with my first copy of *Twenty Thousand Leagues Under the Sea*.

No matter how inspired the vision, dealing with the devil found in the details of creating it, and the uncertainty of "putting it out there" for others to judge, requires tremendous encouragement. For me, the source for that support is my wife, Marcia, who always listens patiently to my stream of consciousness that follows the words, "I have an idea…"

AUTHOR'S NOTE

Like many boys of a certain age, I discovered Jules Verne and was captivated, not just by the tales of scientific adventure, but by the example of the power of imagination to shape what might be possible with the creative application of technology. Who can say with surety what influence it had, but I became qualified as a nuclear submarine engineer and deep submersible pilot. With a career spent in technical realms, I have found in this project a delightful synthesis of my passion for science, history, and the creative arts while re-discovering a boyhood inspiration. Surely Verne would approve. I'd like to dedicate this labor of love to my son, Leo, and to all those for whom submarine dreams stir the child within.

Demetri Capetanopoulos

Inspired by reading *Twenty Thousand Leagues Under the Sea* as a boy, Simon Lake emerged as a competitor to John Holland, and in 1898 made the first successful open-sea voyage in a submarine boat. On that occasion, his submersible, the *Argonaut*—launched at Baltimore in 1897—traveled from Norfolk, Virginia to New York, running awash through a storm that sank some 200 other ships.[144] Jules Verne celebrated the historical occurrence on August 21, 1898, by sending the following cablegram to Mr. Lake.

A-8

Form No. 168.

THE WESTERN UNION TELEGRAPH COMPANY.

INCORPORATED

21,000 OFFICES IN AMERICA. CABLE SERVICE TO ALL THE WORLD.

This Company TRANSMITS and DELIVERS messages only on conditions limiting its liability, which have been assented to by the sender of the following message. Errors can be guarded against only by repeating a message back to the sending station for comparison, and the Company will not hold itself liable for errors or delays in transmission or delivery of Unrepeated Messages, beyond the amount of tolls paid thereon, nor in any case where the claim is not presented in writing within sixty days after the message is filed with the Company for transmission.
This is an UNREPEATED MESSAGE, and is delivered by request of the sender, under the conditions named above.

THOS. T. ECKERT, President and General Manager.

RECEIVED at The Western Union Bldg., 195 Broadway, New York, NY

While my book 'Twenty Thousand Leagues Under the Sea' is entirely a work of imagination, my conviction is that all I said in it will come to pass. A thousand mile voyage in the Baltimore submarine boat is evidence of this. This conspicuous success of submarine navigation in the united states will push on under-water navigation all over the world.

If such a successful test had come a few months earlier it might have played a great part in the war just closed. The next great war may be largely a contest between submarine boats. I think that electricity rather than compressed air will be the motive power in such vessels for the sea is full of this element. It is waiting to be harnessed as steam has been. It will then not be necessary to go to the land for fuel any more than for provisions. The sea will supply food for man and power without limit.

Submarine navigation is now ahead of aerial navigation and will advance much faster from now on. Before the united states gains her full development she is likely to have mighty navies not only on the bosom of the Atlantic and Pacific, but in the upper air and beneath the water's surface.

Jules Verne

Profits from the sale of this
book will be shared with the

DOLPHIN
SCHOLARSHIP
FOUNDATION

Easing the Financial Burden of Undergraduate and
Vocational Education for Eligible Members of the U.S.
Submarine Force and Their Dependents.

www.dolphinscholarship.org